IM

COLLINS

W
A N D
G

Books are on loan for 21 days from date of issue.

Fines for overdue books: 10p for each week or portion of a week plus cost of postage incurred in recovery.

COLLINS

WIRING
AND LIGHTING

ALBERT JACKSON & DAVID DAY

HarperCollins*Publishers*

118,053 £ 10.65.

Published by HarperCollins*Publishers,*
London

First published in 1988
This edition published in 1999
Reprinted 1999, 2000
Most of the text and illustrations in this
book were previously published in the
Collins Complete DIY Manual

ISBN 0 00 414067 2

Copyright © 1988, 1995, 1999
HarperCollins*Publishers*

This book was created exclusively for
HarperCollins*Publishers* by Jackson Day
Jennings Ltd trading as Inklink

Text:
Albert Jackson & David Day

Editorial Director:
Albert Jackson

Consultants:
John Dees & Bob Cole

Text editors:
Diana Volwes & Peter Leek

Executive art director:
Simon Jennings

Design and art direction:
Alan Marshall

Additional design:
Amanda Allchin

Production assistant:
Simon Pickford

Illustrations editor:
David Day

Illustrators:
Robin Harris & David Day

Additional illustrations:
Brian Craker, Michael Parr
& Brian Sayers

Photographer:
Paul Chave

Proofreaders:
Mary Morton & Alison Turnball

Photographic credits
(L = left, R = right, C = centre):

Paul Chave: 12, 13, 14, 15, 17L, 19, 20, 23, 27L,
27R, 28, 29, 34, 36, 37, 40, 46, 49, 54;
Creda Ltd: 59;
Robin Harris: 17R, 22L, 27C;
Neil Waving: 9, 18, 22R, 35, 38, 39, 41, 43, 44

Cover credits:
Top: Jon Bouchier/Elizabeth Whiting &
Associates
Bottom: Mark Luscombe-Whyte

The CIP catalogue record for this book is
available from the British Library

Text set in Univers Condensed and Bodoni
by Inklink, London

Imagesetting by TD Studio, London

Colour origination by Colourscan, Singapore

Printed and bound in Hong Kong

PLEASE NOTE
Great care has been taken to ensure that
the information contained in this book is
accurate. However, the law concerning
Building Regulations, planning, local bylaws
and related matters is neither static nor
simple. A book of this nature cannot replace
specialist advice in appropriate cases and
therefore no responsibility can be accepted
by the publisher or by the authors for any
loss or damage caused by reliance upon the
accuracy of such information.

CONTENTS

Cross-references

Since there are few DIY projects that do not require a combination of skills, you might have to refer to more than one section of this book. The list of cross-references in the margin will help you locate relevant sections or specific information related to the job in hand.

ECONOMICS	6
BASICS	8
SAFETY	9
BASIC REPAIRS	12
FUSE BOARDS	16
CIRCUITS	21
CABLES	22
CHECKLISTS	26
POWER CIRCUITS	28
FIXED APPLIANCES	34
HEATERS	35
KITCHEN APPLIANCES	36
SHAVER SOCKETS	36
COOKERS	37
IMMERSION HEATERS	38
STORAGE HEATERS	40
DOORBELLS	42
TV AERIALS	43
TELEPHONE EXTENSIONS	44
LIGHTING	45
EXTERIOR ELECTRICS	54
COMPLETE WIRING	58
STORAGE HEATERS – CHOICES	59
TOOLS & SKILLS	60
GLOSSARY OF TERMS	61
INDEX	62

SEE ALSO

Details for:

Immersion heaters 38–39

Storage heaters 59

Pressures from all sides urge us to conserve energy – and this applies just as much to electricity as to fossil fuels such as coal, oil and gas. But even without such encouragement, our quarterly electricity bills would provide stimulus enough to make us find ways of using less power.

Nobody wants to live in a poorly heated, dismally lit house without the comforts of hot water, refrigerators, television and other conveniences – but it is often possible to identify where energy is wasted and then find ways to reduce waste without compromising your comfort or pleasure.

Avoid false economy

Whether you do your own wiring or employ a professional, don't attempt to economize by installing fewer sockets than you really need. When you rewire a room, fit as many as you may possibly use. The inconvenience and expense later on of running extra cable and disturbing decoration will far outweigh the cost of an extra socket or two.

Similarly, don't restrict your use of lighting unnecessarily. It uses relatively little power, so it isn't worth risking accidents – for example, on badly lit stairs. Nor need you strain your eyes in the glare from a single light hanging from the ceiling, when extra lighting can provide comfortable and attractive background illumination where needed.

Fitting controls to save money

As the chart opposite clearly shows, heating is by far the biggest consumer of domestic power. One way to reduce your electricity bills is to fit devices that regulate the heating in your home to suit your life style, maintaining comfortable but economic temperatures.

Thermostats
Most modern heating has some form of thermostatic control – a device that will switch power off when surroundings reach a certain temperature. Many thermostats are marked out simply to increase or decrease the temperature, in which case you have to experiment with various settings to find the one that suits you. If the thermostat settings are more precise, try 18°C (65°F) for everyday use – although elderly people are more comfortable at about 21°C (70°F).

As well as saving you money, an immersion-heater thermostat prevents your water from becoming dangerously hot. Set it at 60°C (140°F). (For Economy 7 setting, see right.)

Time switches
Even when thermostatically controlled, heating is expensive if run continuously – but an automatic time switch can turn it on and off at preset times, so that you get up in the morning and arrive home in the evening to a warm house. Set it to turn off the heating about half an hour before you leave home or go to bed, as the house will take time to cool down.

A similar device will ensure that your water is at its hottest when needed.

Recording consumption
Keep an accurate record of your energy saving by taking weekly readings. Note the dates of any measures taken to cut power consumption and compare the corresponding drop in meter readings.

Digital meters
Modern meters display a row of figures or digits that represent the total number of units consumed since the meter was installed. To calculate the number of units used since your last electricity bill, simply subtract the 'present reading' shown on your bill from the number of units now shown on the meter. Make sure that the bill gives an actual reading and not an estimate (which is indicated by the letter 'E' before the reading).

● **Insulation**
Measures taken to save energy will have little effect unless you insulate your house as well as the hot-water cylinder and pipework. You can do most of the work yourself without much cost or effort.

ECONOMICAL OFF-PEAK RATES

Electricity is normally sold at a general-purpose rate, every unit used costing the same; but if you warm your home with storage heaters and heat your water electrically, then you can take advantage of the economical off-peak tariff. This system, called Economy 7, allows you to charge storage heaters and heat water at less than half the general-purpose rate for seven hours, starting between midnight and 1 a.m. Other appliances used during that time get cheap power too, so more savings can be made by running the dishwasher or washing machine after you've gone to bed. Each appliance must, of course, be fitted with a timer. The Economy 7 daytime rate is higher than the general-purpose one, but the cost of running 24-hour appliances such as freezers and refrigerators is balanced since they also use cheap power for seven hours.

For full benefit from off-peak water heating use a 182 to 227 litre (40 to 50 gallon) cylinder, to store as much cheap hot water as possible. You will need a twin-element heater or two separate units. One heater, near the base of the cylinder, heats the whole tank on cheap power; another, about half way up, tops up the hot water during the day. Set the night-time heater at 75°C (167°F), the daytime one at 60°C (140°F).

The Electricity Companies provide Economy 7 customers with a special meter to record daytime and night-time consumption separately, plus a timer that automatically switches the supply from one rate to the other.

HOW TO READ DIAL METERS

The principle of a dial meter is simple. Ignore the dial marked 1/10, which is only for testing. Start with the dial indicating single units (kWh) and, working from right to left, record the readings from the 10, 100, 1000 and finally 10,000 unit dials. Note the digits the pointers have passed. If a pointer is, say, between 5 and 6, record 5. If it is right on a number, say 8, check the next dial on the right: if that pointer is between 9 and 0, record 7; if it's past 0, record 8. Also, remember that adjacent dials revolve in opposite directions, alternating along the row.

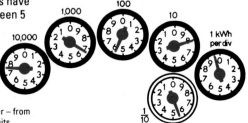

Reading a dial meter
Write down your reading in reverse order – from right to left. This meter records 76,579 units.

Apart from the standing charge and any hire-purchase payments, your electricity bill is based on the number of units of electricity you have consumed during a given period. Each unit represents the amount used in one hour by a 1kW appliance. An appliance rated at 3kW will use the same amount of energy in 20 minutes.

TYPICAL RUNNING COSTS

	Appliance	Typical usage	No. of units		Appliance	Typical usage	No. of units
	Cooker	Cooks 1 day's meal for four people.	2½		Iron	In use for 2 hours.	1
	Microwave	Cooks 2 joints of meat.	1		Vacuum cleaner	Works for 1½–2 hours.	1
	Slow cooker	Cooks for 8 hours.	1		Cooker hood	Runs for 24 hours continuously.	2
	Storage heater (2kW)	Provides 1 day's heating.	11		Extractor fan	Runs for 24 hours continuously.	1
	Bar fire or fan heater (2kW)	Provides heat for 1 hour.	2		Hair dryer	Runs for 2 hours.	1
	Immersion heater	Supplies 1 day's hot water for a family of four.	9		Shaver	Gives 1800 shaves.	1
	Instant water heater	Heats 2 to 3 bowls of washing-up water.	1		Single overblanket	Warms the bed for 1 week.	2
	Instant shower	Gives 1 to 2 showers.	1		Single underblanket	Warms the bed for 1 week.	1
	Dishwasher	Washes 1 full load.	2		Power drill	Works for 4 hours.	1
	Automatic washing machine	Washes 1 full load with prewash.	2½		Hedge trimmer	Trims for 2½ hours.	1
	Tumble dryer	Dries 1 full load.	2½		Cylinder lawn mower	Cuts grass for 3 hours.	1
	4 cu ft refrigerator	Keeps food fresh for 1 week.	7		Hover mower	Cuts grass for 1 hour.	1
	6 cu ft freezer	Maintains required temperature for 1 week.	9		Stereo system	Plays for 8 hours.	1
	Heated towel rail	Warms continuously for 4 hours.	1		Colour TV	Provides 6 hours' viewing.	1
	Electric kettle	Boils 40 cups of tea.	1		VCR	Records for 10 hours.	1
	Coffee percolator	Makes 75 cups of coffee.	1		100W bulb	Gives 10 hours' illumination.	1
	Toaster	Toasts 70 slices of bread.	1		40W fluorescent strip light	Provides 20 hours' illumination.	1

SEE ALSO

Details for:	
Electric heaters	35
Heated towel rail	35
Instant water heater	36
Wiring cooker hood	36
Wiring extractor fan	36
Wiring kitchen appliances	36
Wiring a cooker	37–38
Immersion heaters	38–39
Storage heaters	40–41, 59
Instant shower	45
Lighting	45–53

● **Typical running costs** The table shows how much electricity is used on average by common household appliances that have different kilowatt (kW) ratings. For example, a 100W light bulb can give you 10 hours of illumination before it uses up a 1kW unit, whereas a 3kW bar fire will give off heat for only 20 minutes for the same 1kW.

SEE ALSO

Details for:	
Earth bonding	10, 17
Flex	12
Fuses	15, 19
Circuits	21
Cable	22
Running cable	23–25

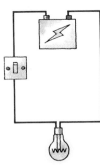

A basic circuit
Electricity runs from the source (battery) to the appliance (bulb) and then returns to the source. A switch breaks the circuit to interrupt the flow of electricity.

Double insulation
A square within a square either printed or moulded on an appliance means it is double-insulated and its flex does not need an earth wire.

Many people imagine that working on the electrical circuits of a house is an extremely complicated business – but the circuitry is, in fact, based on very simple principles.

For any electrical appliance to work, the power must have a complete circuit – the electricity must be able to flow along a wire from its source (a battery, for instance) to the appliance (say a light bulb) and then back to the source along another wire. If the circuit is broken at any point, the appliance will stop working – the bulb will go out.

Breaking the circuit – and restoring it as required – is what a switch is for. When the switch is in the 'on' position, the circuit is complete and the bulb or other appliance operates. Turning the switch off makes a gap in the circuit, so the electricity stops flowing. Although a break in either of the two wires would stop the power flow, a switch must always be wired so that it interrupts the live wire – the one that takes power to the appliance. In this way the appliance is completely dead when the switch is off. If the switch is wired to interrupt the neutral wire, which takes the electricity back to its source, the appliance will stop working but elements in it will still remain 'live' – which can be dangerous.

Although mains electricity is much more powerful than that produced by a battery, it operates in exactly the same way, flowing through a live or 'phase' wire linked to every socket outlet, light and fixed electrical appliance in your home. For purposes of identification the covering of live wires is coloured red or brown. The covering of the neutral wires, which take the current back out of the house, is either black or blue.

Identifying conductors ▶
The insulation used to cover the conductors in electrical cable and flex is colour-coded to indicate live, neutral and earth.

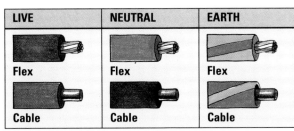

LIVE	NEUTRAL	EARTH
Flex	Flex	Flex
Cable	Cable	Cable

Earthing

Any material through which electricity can flow is known as a conductor. Most metals conduct electricity well – which is why metal (most often copper, as it is probably the most efficient conductor of electricity) is used for electrical wiring.

However, the earth itself, the ground on which we stand, is also an extremely good conductor. In fact, it is an even better conductor than the wiring that's used for electrical circuits – which is why electricity will always flow into the earth, if it has an opportunity to do so, by the shortest available route. This means that if you were to touch a live conductor, the current would divert and take the short route through your body to the earth – perhaps with fatal results.

A similar thing can occur if a live wire comes accidentally into contact with any exposed metal component of an appliance, including its casing. To prevent this, a third wire is included in the wiring system and connected to the earth, usually via the outer casing of the Electricity Company's main service cable. This third wire – called the earth wire – is attached to the metal casing of some appliances and to special earth terminals in others, providing a direct route to the ground should a fault occur. This sudden change of route by the electricity – known as an earth fault – causes a fuse to blow or circuit breaker to operate, cutting off the current.

Appliances that are double-insulated – which usually means they have a non-conductive plastic casing that insulates the user from metal parts that could become live – must not be be earthed with a third wire.

The earth wire either has a green-and-yellow covering or is a bare copper wire sandwiched between the insulated live and neutral wires in an electrical cable. Whenever a bare earth wire is exposed for linking to socket outlets or lighting fittings, it should be covered with a green-and-yellow sleeve.

Metal pipes must also be connected to the earthing system by a separate cable to ensure they do not precipitate an accident during the time it would take for a fault to blow a fuse.

DIY WIRING

Many householders are reluctant to undertake any but the simplest jobs involving electricity, no matter how competent they may be in other areas of home improvement.

To some extent this attitude is quite justifiable. After all, it is sensible to have a healthy respect for anything as potentially dangerous as electricity, and it would be very foolhardy of anyone to jump in at the deep end and undertake a major installation before gaining some experience on less ambitious jobs.

In the end, though, many of us are driven to doing our own house wiring simply by the prohibitive cost of hiring professionals. Nobody minds paying for expert skill and knowledge, but the truth is that much of the expert's time is taken up lifting floorboards, chopping out and repairing plaster, and drilling holes in walls and timbers to run the cable – all jobs that most people would be happy to do themselves.

The electrician's 'bible'
What unnerves the householder is the possibility of making mistakes with the connections or with the choice of equipment. Fortunately, in Britain we are guided by detailed rules laid down by the Institution of Electrical Engineers in a document known as the IEE Wiring Regulations. This is the professional electrician's 'bible', and it covers every aspect of electrical installation. If you follow its recommendations carefully, then you can feel confident that your wiring work will be safe.

You can buy a copy of the Wiring Regulations, or you may be able to borrow one from your public library. However, the Regulations themselves are notoriously difficult to understand, and it has even proved necessary to publish a 'guide to the guide' so that electricians can find their way through this exacting reference book.

The methods suggested in these pages comply with the Regulations, so you should have no need to refer to the originals unless you plan to undertake a job beyond the scope of this book.

Nevertheless, take the trouble to read all the relevant information in this chapter so that you fully understand what you are doing – and if at any time you feel unsure of your competence, then don't hesitate to ask a professional electrician for help or advice.

FUSES AND CIRCUIT BREAKERS

A conductor will heat up if an unusually powerful current flows through it. This can damage electrical equipment and create a serious fire risk if it is allowed to continue in any part of the domestic wiring system. As a safeguard, weak links are included in the wiring to break the circuit before the current reaches a dangerously high level.

The most common form of protection is a fuse, a thin wire that's designed to break the circuit by melting at a specific current. This varies according to the part of the system that the fuse is protecting – an individual appliance, a single power or lighting circuit, or the entire domestic wiring system.

Alternatively, a special switch called a circuit breaker is used that trips and cuts off the current as soon as an overload on the wiring is detected.

A fuse will 'blow' in the following circumstances:
- If too many appliances are operated on a circuit simultaneously, then the excessive demand for electricity will blow the fuse in that circuit.
- If the current reroutes to earth due to a faulty appliance, the flow of power increases in the circuit and blows the fuse (this is known as an earth fault).

WARNING: The original fault must be dealt with before the fuse is replaced.

Measuring electricity

Watts measure the amount of power used by an appliance when working. The wattage of an electrical appliance is normally marked on its casing.

One thousand watts (1000W) equal one kilowatt (1kW).

Amps measure the flow of current that is necessary to produce the required wattage for an appliance.

Volts measure the 'pressure' provided by the generators of the Electricity Company that drives the current along the conductors to the various outlets. In Britain 240 volts is standard.

If you know two of these measurements, you can determine the other one:

$\dfrac{\text{Watts}}{\text{Volts}}$ = Amps	Amps x Volts = Watts
Use this method to determine what kind of fuse or flex is safe.	Indicates how much power is needed to operate an appliance.

Throughout this chapter you will find many references to the need for safety while working on any part of your electrical system, but it cannot be stressed too strongly that you must also take every step possible to safeguard yourself and others who will later be using the system. Faulty wiring and appliances are dangerous, and can be lethal. Whenever you are dealing with electricity, the rule must be 'safety first'.

- Never inspect or work on any part of an electrical installation without first switching off the power at the consumer unit and removing the relevant circuit fuse.
- Always unplug a portable electrical appliance or light fitting before doing any work on it.
- Always double-check all your work (especially connections) before you turn the electricity on again.
- Always use the correct tools for an electrical job, and use good-quality equipment and materials.
- Fuses are vital safety devices. Never fit one that's rated too highly for the circuit it is to protect – and never be tempted to use any other type of wire or metal strip in place of proper fuses or fuse wire.
- Wear rubber-soled shoes when you're working on an electrical installation.

Using professionals

Always seek the advice and/or help of a professional electrician if you don't feel competent to handle a particular job yourself – especially if you discover or even only suspect that some part of an installation is out of date, or that it may be dangerous for some other reason.

Make sure that any professional you hire is fully qualified. Check whether he or she is registered with the NICEIC (the National Inspection Council for Electrical Installation Contracting). To be a member of this association an electrician has to be fully cognizant of the Wiring Regulations – published by the Institution of Electrical Engineers – and must ensure that his or her work complies with them.

Testing an installation

Any significant rewiring, especially new circuits, must be tested by a competent electrician – indeed, when you apply for connection to the mains supply you have to submit a certificate to the Electricity Company confirming that the new wiring complies with the Wiring Regulations.

For a fee, the Electricity Company will test DIY wiring at the time of connection. Never attempt to make connections to the meter or Company's earth terminal yourself. If you aren't sure whether new wiring requires testing, contact your local Electricity Company for advice.

IS THE POWER OFF?

Having turned off the power, you can make doubly sure that a particular accessory is safe to work on by using an electronic two-probe mains-voltage tester to check whether terminals or wires are live before tampering with them. Always make sure the tester itself is functioning properly before and after you use it by testing it on a circuit you know to be live.

Following the maker's instructions, put one probe on the neutral terminal and the other on the live terminal to be tested; if the bulb lights up, the circuit is live. If it does not illuminate, test again between the earth terminal and each of the live and neutral terminals. If the bulb still doesn't light up, you can assume the circuit isn't live – providing that you have checked the tester.

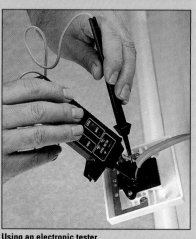

Using an electronic tester
Touch the neutral terminal with one probe and the live terminal with the other. The circuit is live if the indicator illuminates.

SEE ALSO	
Details for:	
Electric shock	11
Fuses	15, 19
Meter	16
Consumer's earth terminal	16-17
Switching off	16, 18
Fuse ratings	19
Electrician's tools	60

BATHROOM SAFETY

SEE ALSO

Details for:

Bonding to earth	16-17
Protective multiple earthing	17
Cables	22
Running cable	23-25
Bathroom heaters	35
Shaver sockets	36
Electric shower	45
Close-mounted lights	47
Ceiling switch	49, 51

● **Supplementary bonding in a kitchen**
Supplementary-bonding regulations apply to kitchens as well as bathrooms. Bond metal sink units, metallic supply and wastepipes, radiators and central-heating pipework. Space and water heaters must be bonded as for bathrooms.

Because water is a highly efficient conductor of electric current, water and electricity form a very dangerous combination. For this reason, bathrooms are potentially the most dangerous areas in your home in terms of electricity. Where there are so many exposed metal pipes and fittings, combined with wet conditions, stringent regulations must be observed if fatal accidents are to be avoided.

GENERAL SAFETY

● No socket outlets should be fitted in a bathroom – except for special ones that are approved for electric shavers and which conform to BS 3535.

● The IEE Wiring Regulations stipulate that any standard light switches in bathrooms must be well out of reach of anyone who is using a shower, bath or washbasin. The best way to comply with this requirement is to fit only ceiling-mounted pull-cord switches.

● Any bathroom heater must comply with the IEE Wiring Regulations.

● If you have a shower unit in a bedroom, it must be not less than 2.5m (8ft) from any socket outlet.

● Light fittings must be well out of reach and shielded, so fit a close-mounted ceiling light, properly enclosed, rather than a pendant fitting.

● Never use a portable fire or other electrical appliance, such as a hair dryer, in a bathroom, even if plugged into a socket outside the room.

WARNING

Have supplementary bonding tested by a qualified electrician. If you have not had any previous experience of wiring and making electrical connections, have supplementary bonding installed by a professional.

Supplementary bonding

In any bathroom there are many non-electrical metallic components, such as metal baths and basins, supply pipes to bath and basin taps, metal wastepipes, radiators, central-heating pipework and so on – all of which could cause an accident during the time it would take for an electrical fault to blow a fuse or operate a miniature circuit breaker (MCB). To ensure that no dangerous voltages are created between metal parts, the Wiring Regulations stipulate that all these metal components must be connected one to another by a conductor which is itself connected to a terminal on the earthing block in the consumer unit. This is known as supplementary bonding and is required for all bathrooms – even when there is no electrical equipment installed in the room and even though the water and gas pipes are bonded to the consumer's earth terminal near the consumer unit.

When electrical equipment such as a heater or shower is fitted in a bathroom, that too must be supplementary-bonded by connecting its metalwork – such as the casing – to the nonelectrical metal pipework, even though the appliance is connected to the earthing conductor in the supply cable.

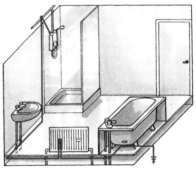

Supplementary bonding in a bathroom

Making the connections

The Wiring Regulations specify the minimum size of earthing conductor that can be used for supplementary bonding in different situations, so that large-scale electrical installations can be costed economically. In a domestic environment, use 6mm^2 single-core cable insulated with green-and-yellow PVC for supplementary bonding. This is large enough to be safe in any domestic situation. For a neat appearance, plan the route of the bonding cable to run from point to point behind the bath panel, under floorboards, and through basin pedestals. If necessary, run the cable through a hollow wall or under plaster like any other electrical cable.

Connecting to pipework
An earth clamp (1) is used for making connections to pipework. Clean the pipe locally with wire wool to make a good connection between the pipe and clamp, and scrape or strip an area of paintwork if the pipe has been painted.

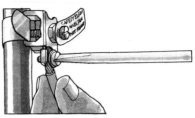

1 Fit an earth clamp to pipework

Connecting to a bath or basin
Metal baths or basins are made with an earth tag. Connect the earth cable by trapping the bared end of the conductor under a nut and bolt with metal washers (2). Make sure the tag has not been painted or enamelled.

If an old metal bath or basin has not been provided with an earth tag, drill a hole through the foot of the bath or through the rim at the back of the basin and connect the cable with a similar nut and bolt with metal washers.

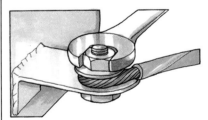

2 Connect to bath or basin earth tag

Connecting to an appliance
Simply connect the earth to the terminal provided in the electrical appliance (3) and run it to a clamp on a metal supply pipe nearby.

3 Fix to the earth terminal in an appliance
The appliance's own earth connection may share the same terminal.

DEALING WITH ELECTRIC SHOCK

If someone in your presence receives an electric shock and is still in contact with its source, turn off the current at once either by pulling out the plug or by switching off at the socket or consumer unit. If this is not possible, don't take hold of the person – or the current may pass through you too. Pull the victim free with a scarf or dry towel or something like that, or knock their hand free of the electrical equipment with a piece of wood. As a last resort, free the victim by taking hold of their loose clothing – but without touching the body.

Don't attempt to move anyone who has fallen as a result of electric shock – except to place them in the recovery position (see right) – as they may have sustained other injuries. Wrap them in a blanket or coat to keep them warm until they can move themselves.

Once the person can move and is no longer in contact with the electrical equipment, treat their electrical burns by reducing the heat of the injury under slowly running cold water. Then apply a dry dressing and seek medical advice.

Isolating the victim
If a person sustains an electric shock, turn off the supply of electricity immediately, either at the consumer unit or at a socket (**1**). If this is not possible, pull the victim free with a dry towel, or knock their hand free of the electrical equipment (**2**) with a piece of wood or a broom.

Severe electric shock can make a person stop breathing. Once you have freed them from the electricity supply (without grasping the victim's body directly – see left), revive them by means of artificial ventilation.

Clear the airway
First, clear the victim's airway. To do this, loosen the clothing round the neck, chest and waist, make sure that the mouth is free of food, and remove loose dentures (**1**).

1 Clear the mouth of food or loose dentures

Lay the person on his or her back and carefully tilt the head back by raising the chin (**2**). This prevents the victim's tongue blocking the airway and may in itself be enough to restart the person's breathing. If it doesn't succeed in doing so quickly, try more direct methods of artificial ventilation.

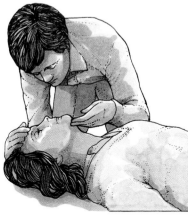

2 Tip the head back to open the airway

Mouth-to-mouth
Keeping the victim's nostrils closed by pinching them between thumb and forefinger, cover the mouth with your own, making a seal all round (**3**). Blow firmly and look for signs of the chest rising. Remove your lips and allow the chest to fall. Repeat this procedure, breathing rhythmically into the mouth every six seconds. After ten breaths, phone the emergency services. Continue with the artificial ventilation till normal breathing resumes or expert help arrives.

Mouth-to-nose
If injuries to the face make mouth-to-mouth ventilation impossible, follow a similar procedure but keep the victim's mouth covered with one hand and blow firmly into the nose (**4**).

3 Mouth-to-mouth   **4 Mouth-to-nose**

Reviving a baby
If the victim is a baby or small child, cover both the nose and the mouth at the same time with your own mouth (**5**) and proceed as for mouth-to-mouth ventilation (see left), but breathe every three seconds.

5 Cover a baby's nose and mouth

Recovery
Once breathing has started again, put the victim in the recovery position. Turn him or her face down with the head turned sideways and tilted up slightly. This keeps the airway open and will also prevent vomit being inhaled if the person is sick.

Lift one leg out from the body and support the head by placing the person's left hand, palm down, under his or her cheek (**6**). Keep the casualty warm with blankets until help arrives.

6 Recovery position

SEE ALSO

Details for:

Colour coding	8
Switching off	16
Fabric-covered flex	46

You can carry out many repairs and replacements without having to concern yourself with the wiring system installed in your home. Many light fittings and appliances are supplied with electricity by means of flexible cords that plug into the system – so provided that they have been disconnected, there can be no risk of getting an electric shock while working on them.

WARNING

Never attempt to carry out electrical repairs without first unplugging the appliance or switching off the power supply at the consumer unit.

Flexible cord (flex)

All portable appliances and some of the smaller fixed ones, as well as pendant and portable light fittings, are connected to your home's permanent wiring system by means of conductors in the form of flexible cord, normally called 'flex'.

Each of the conductors in any type of flex is made up of numerous fine wires twisted together, and each conductor is insulated from the others by a covering of plastic insulation. So that the conductors can be identified easily, the insulation is usually colour-coded (brown = live; blue = neutral; and green-and-yellow = earth).

Further protection is provided on most flexible cords in the form of an outer sheathing of insulating material enclosing the inner conductors.

Heat-resistant flex is available for enclosed light fittings and appliances whose surfaces will become hot.

COILED FLEX

A coiled flex that stretches and retracts can be a convenient way of connecting a portable lamp or appliance.

Coiled flex is sold as a standard length

TYPES OF ELECTRICAL FLEX

Parallel twin

Parallel twin flex has two conductors insulated with PVC (polyvinyl chloride) running side by side. The insulation material is joined between the two conductors along the length of the flex. This kind of flex should only be used for extra-low-voltage (bell) wiring or inside certain types of light fitting. The wires are hardly ever colour-coded.

Twisted twin

This is similar to parallel twin flex, but the PVC-insulated conductors are twisted together for extra strength. It was once used to support hanging light fittings, but nowadays must be replaced with a two-core sheathed flex when wiring pendant lights. Also, any old rubber-insulated flex with braided-cotton covering, which is still found in some homes, should be replaced.

Flat twin sheathed

Flat twin sheathed flex has colour-coded live and neutral conductors inside a PVC sheathing. This flex is used for double-insulated light fittings and small appliances.

Two-core circular sheathed

This has colour-coded neutral and live conductors inside a PVC sheathing that is circular in its cross section. It is used for wiring certain pendant lights and some double-insulated appliances.

Three-core circular sheathed

This is like two-core circular sheathed flex, but it also contains an insulated and colour-coded earth wire. This flex is perhaps the most commonly used for all kinds of appliances.

Unkinkable braided

This flex is used for appliances such as kettles and irons, which are of a high wattage and whose flex must stand up to movement and wear. The three rubber-insulated conductors, plus the textile cords that run parallel with them, are all contained in a rubber sheathing that is bound outside with braided material. This type of flex can be wound round the handle of a cool electric iron.

Although the spacing of terminals in plugs and appliances varies, the method of stripping and connecting the flex is the same.

Stripping the flex

If the flex is sheathed, slit the sheath lengthwise with a sharp knife (1), being careful not to cut into the insulation covering the individual conductors. Divide the conductors of parallel twin flex by pulling them apart before you expose their ends.

Peel the sheathing away from the conductors, then fold it back over the knife blade and cut it off (2).

Separate the conductors, crop them to length and, using wire strippers, remove about 12mm (½in) of insulation from the end of each one (3).

MULTI-PURPOSE TOOL

A multi-purpose tool will crop and strip any size of cable or flex.

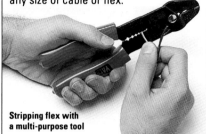

Stripping flex with
a multi-purpose tool

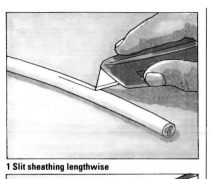

1 Slit sheathing lengthwise

2 Fold sheathing over the blade and cut it off

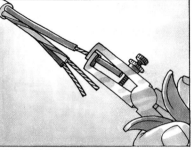

3 Strip insulation from conductors

Connecting the conductors

Twist together the individual filaments of each conductor to make them neat.

If the plug or appliance has post-type terminals, fold the bared end of wire (1) before pushing it in the hole. Make sure the insulation butts against the post and that all the wire filaments are enclosed within the terminal. Then tighten the clamping screw, and pull gently on the wire to make sure it is held quite firmly.

1 Post terminal

When you're connecting to clamp-type terminals, wrap the bared wire round the post clockwise (2), then screw the clamping nut down tight on the wire. After tightening the nut, check that the conductor is held securely.

2 Clamp terminal

Details for:	
Measuring electricity	9
Immersion heaters	39
Wire strippers	60

CHOOSING A FLEX

Not only is the right type of flex for the job important; the size of its conductors must suit the amount of current that will be used by the appliance.

Flex is rated according to the area of the cross section of its conductors, 0.5mm² being the smallest for normal domestic wiring. The flex size required is determined by the flow of current that it can handle safely. Excessive current will make a conductor overheat, so the size of the flex must be matched to the power (wattage) of the appliance which it is feeding.

Manufacturers frequently fit 1.25mm² flex to appliances of less than 3000W (3kW), since it is safer to use a larger conductor than necessary if a smaller flex might be easily damaged. Adopt the same procedure when replacing flex.

Conductor	Current rating	Appliance
0.5mm²	3amp	Light fittings up to 720W
0.75mm²	6amp	Light fittings and appliances up to 1440W
1.0mm²	10amp	Appliances up to 2400W
1.25mm²	13amp	Appliances up to 3120W
1.5mm²	15amp	Appliances up to 3600W
2.5mm²	20amp	Appliances up to 4800W
4.0mm²	25amp	Appliances up to 6000W

● Flex for immersion heaters
Because they generate relatively high background temperatures, 3kW immersion heaters are wired with 2.5mm² heat-resistant flex (see WIRING AN IMMERSION HEATER).

EXTENDING
FLEXIBLE CORD

SEE ALSO
Details for:
Flex   12
Connecting flex   13
Positioning sockets   28

When you plan the positions of socket outlets, try to ensure there will be enough, all conveniently situated, so that it is never necessary to extend the flexible cord of a table lamp or other appliance. But if you do find that a flex will not reach a socket, extend it so that it is not stretched taut, which can cause an accident. Never join two lengths of flex by twisting the bared ends of wires together, even if you bind them with insulating tape. People often do this as a temporary measure then neglect to make a proper connection later, which can have fatal consequences.

Flex connectors

If possible, fit a longer flex, wiring it into the appliance itself. But if you can't do this or don't want to dismantle the appliance, use a flex connector. There are two-terminal and three-terminal connectors, which you should match to the type of flex you are using. Never join two-core flex to three-core flex.

Strip off just enough sheathing so that the conductors can reach the terminals and the sheathed part of each cord will be secured under the cord clamp at each end of the connector.

Cut the conductors to length with engineer's pliers. Strip and connect the conductors; connect the live conductor to one of the outer terminals, the neutral to the other, and the earth wire (if present) to the central one. Make sure that matching conductors of the two cords are connected to the same terminals, then tighten the cord clamps and screw the cover in place.

In-line switches
If you plan to fit a longer continuous length of flex you can install an in-line switch that will allow you to control the appliance or light fitting from some distance away – a great advantage for the elderly or bed-ridden. Some in-line switches are fluorescent.

Wiring a flex connector

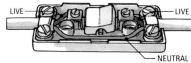

Wiring an in-line switch

Extension leads

If you fit a long flex to a power tool it will inevitably become tangled and one of the conductors will eventually break, perhaps causing a short circuit. The solution is to buy an extension lead or make one yourself.

The best type of extension lead to be had commercially is wound on a drum. There are 5amp ones – but it's safer to buy one with a 13amp rating, so that you can run a wider range of equipment without danger of overloading. If you use such a lead while it is wound on the drum it may overheat, so develop the habit of fully unwinding it each time (see left). The drums of these leads have a built-in 13amp socket to take the plug of the appliance; the plug on the lead is then connected to a wall socket.

You can make an extension lead from a length of 1.5mm^2 three-core flex with a standard 13amp plug on one end and a trailing socket on the other. Use those with unbreakable rubber casings. A trailing socket is wired in a similar way to a 13amp plug (see opposite). Its terminals are marked to indicate which conductors to connect to them.

'Multi-way' trailing sockets will take several plugs and are ideal for hi-fi systems or computers with individual components that need to be connected to the mains supply. Using a multi-way socket, the whole system is supplied from a single plug in the wall socket.

You can also extend a lead by using a lightweight two-part flex connector. One half has three pins that fit into the other half of the connector.

Unwind a lead
Always fully unwind a 13amp extension lead before you plug in an appliance rated at 1kW or more.

WARNING

When wiring a two-part flex connector never attach the part with the pins to the extension lead. The exposed pins will become live – and dangerous – when the lead is plugged into the socket. In fact nothing electrical should ever be wired so that a plug can become live other than when its pins are concealed in a socket.

TYPES OF FLEX EXTENDER

Below are illustrated four of the devices available for extending the flexible cords of electrical appliances.

Drum-type extension lead

13amp plug and trailing socket

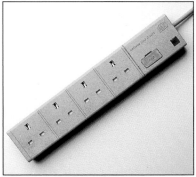

Multi-way trailing socket

Two-part flex connector

In the past there were many types of plug, but today standard 13amp square-pin plugs are used for all portable appliances and light fittings. They are available with rigid plastic or unbreakable rubber casings. Some have integral neon indicators to show when they are live, and some have pins insulated for part of their length to prevent the user getting a shock from a plug pulled partly from the socket.

Safety standards and fuses

Use only plugs marked BS 1363, which conform to British Standards. Square-pin plugs have to have a small cartridge fuse to protect the appliance. Use a 3amp (red) fuse for appliances of up to 720W, and a 13amp (brown) fuse for those of 720 to 3000W (3kW). There are also 2, 5 and 10amp fuses, but these are less often used in the home.

Wiring a 13amp plug

Loosen the large screw between the pins and remove the cover. Position the flex on the open plug to gauge how much sheathing to remove (remember that the cord clamp must grip sheathed flex, not the conductors).

Strip the sheathing and position the flex on the plug again, so that you can cut the conductors to the right length. These should take the most direct routes to their terminals and lie neatly in the channels of the plug.

Strip and prepare the ends of the wires, then secure each to its terminal. If you are using two-core flex, wire to the live and neutral terminals, leaving the earth terminal empty.

Tighten the cord clamp to grip the end of the sheathing and secure the flex (one type of plug has a sprung cord grip that tightens if the flex is pulled hard). Check that a fuse of the correct rating is fitted, then replace the plug's cover and tighten up the screw.

Wiring older plugs

If your home still has old round-pin sockets, they will only take round-pin plugs, which are not fused. Use 2amp plugs for lighting only; 5amp plugs for appliances of up to 1kW; and 15amp plugs for appliances between 1kW and 3kW. Have your wiring upgraded as soon as possible, so that you can use modern fused square-pin plugs.

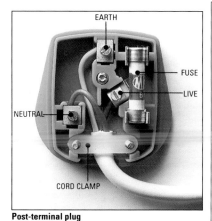
Post-terminal plug

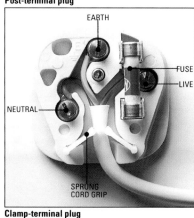
Clamp-terminal plug

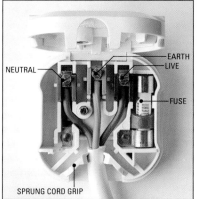
Some plugs have colour-coded terminals

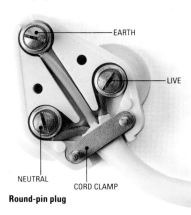
Round-pin plug

REPLACING A PENDANT LAMPHOLDER

Because they are not easy to inspect, damaged pendant lampholders often go unnoticed, so check their condition from time to time and replace any that look suspect before they become dangerous.

Pendant lampholders, which hang on flex from the ceiling, are in a stream of hot air rising from the bulb, and in time this can make plastic holders brittle and more easily cracked or broken. On a metal lampholder, the earth wire can become detached or corroded so that the fitting is no longer safe.

Types of lampholder

Plastic lampholders are the most common. These have a threaded skirt that screws onto the actual holder, the part that takes the bulb, and some versions have an extended skirt for fitting in bathrooms. You should fit heat-resistant plastic holders if you use a close-fitting or badly ventilated shade.

Plastic holders are designed to take two-core flex only. Never fit one on a three-core flex, as there is no place to attach the earth wire.

Metal lampholders are similar in their construction, but they must be wired with three-core flex so that they can be connected to earth. Never fit a metal lampholder in a bathroom, and never attach one to a two-core flex, which has no earth conductor.

Fitting a lampholder

Before commencing work, remove the circuit fuse or circuit breaker from the consumer unit so that no-one can turn the power on. Unscrew the old holder's cap – or the retaining ring if it's a metal one – and slide it up the flex to expose the terminals. Loosen their screws and pull the wires out. If some wires are broken or brittle, cut back slightly to expose sound wires before fitting the new holder.

Slide the cap of the new fitting up the flex and attach it temporarily with adhesive tape. Fit the live wire into one of the terminals, and the neutral wire into the other. Then loop the conductors round the supporting lugs of the holder, to take the weight off the terminals, and screw the cap down.

On a metal holder, pass the earth wire through the hole in the cap before you secure it. Connect the earth wire to the earth terminal, then secure the cap with the retaining ring.

Details for:	
Flex	12
Connecting flex	13
Switching off	16

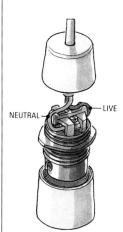
Wiring a plastic pendant lampholder

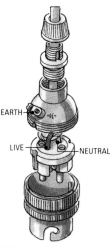
Wiring a metal pendant lampholder

15

SEE ALSO

Details for:

Cheap electricity	6
Consumer unit	18
Fuses	19
Circuit breakers	19, 20
Switchfuse unit	38
Storage heaters	40-41

Electricity flows because of a difference in 'pressure' between the live wire and the neutral one, and this difference in pressure is measured in volts.

Domestic electricity in Britain is supplied at 240 volts 'alternating current' by way of the Electricity Company's main service cable, which normally enters your house underground, although in some areas electricity is distributed by overhead cables.

The service head

The main cable terminates at the service head, or cutout, which contains the service fuse. This fuse prevents the neighbourhood's supply being affected if there should be a serious fault in the circuitry of your house. Cables connect the cutout to the meter, which registers how much electricity you consume. Both the meter and cutout belong to the Electricity Company and must not be tampered with. The meter is sealed in order to disclose interference.

If you use cheap night-time power for storage heaters and hot water, a time switch will be mounted between the cutout and the meter.

Consumer units

Electricity is fed to and from the consumer unit by 'meter leads', thick single-core insulated-and-sheathed cables made up of several wires twisted together. The consumer unit is a box that contains the fuseways which protect the individual circuits in the house. It also incorporates the main isolating switch, which you operate when you need to cut off the supply of power to the whole house.

In a house where several new circuits have been installed over the years, the number of circuits may exceed the number of fuseways in the consumer unit, so an individual switchfuse unit – or more than one – may have to be mounted alongside the main unit. Switchfuse units comprise a single fuseway and an isolating switch. They too are connected to the meter by means of meter leads.

If your home is heated by off-peak storage heaters, then you will have an Economy 7 meter and a separate consumer unit for the circuits that supply the heaters.

● **Main isolating switch**
Not all main isolating switches operate in the same way. Before you need to use it, check whether the main switch on your consumer unit should be up or down for 'off'.

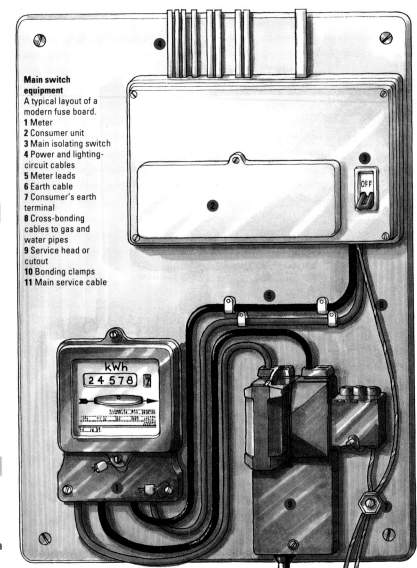

Main switch equipment
A typical layout of a modern fuse board.
1 Meter
2 Consumer unit
3 Main isolating switch
4 Power and lighting-circuit cables
5 Meter leads
6 Earth cable
7 Consumer's earth terminal
8 Cross-bonding cables to gas and water pipes
9 Service head or cutout
10 Bonding clamps
11 Main service cable

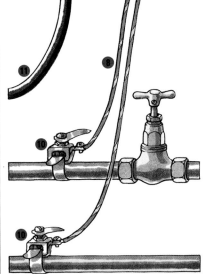

SWITCHING OFF THE POWER

In an emergency, switch off the supply of electricity to the entire house by operating the main isolating switch on the consumer unit.

Before working on any part of the electrical system of your home, always operate the main isolating switch and then remove the individual circuit fuse or miniature circuit breaker (MCB) that will cut off the power to the relevant circuit. That circuit will then be safe to work on, even if you restore the power to the rest of the house by operating the main switch again.

The earthing system

All of the individual earth conductors of the various circuits in the house are connected to a metal earthing block in the consumer unit. A single cable with a green-and-yellow covering runs from this earthing block to the consumer's earth terminal, which is mounted next to the cutout. In most urban houses a connection is provided from inside the cutout to an external earth-connection block, which is also wired to the consumer's earth terminal. This provides an effective path to earth – the current will pass along the sheath of the main service cable to the Electricity Company's substation, where it is solidly connected to earth.

In the past, most domestic electrical systems were earthed to the cold-water supply, so that earth-leakage current passed out along the metal water pipes into the ground in which they were buried. But nowadays more and more water systems use nonmetallic, nonconductive pipes and fittings, so that means of earthing is no longer reliable. Despite this, you will find that your gas and water pipework is connected to the consumer's earth terminal. This ensures that both water and gas piping systems are cross-bonded so that earth-leakage current passing through either system will run without hindrance to the main earth without creating dangerously high voltages. The cross-bonding clamps must be as close as possible to the point where the pipes enter the house but on the consumer's side (within 600mm) of the stopcock or gas meter.

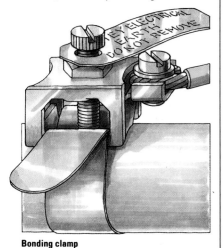

Bonding clamp
This type of clamp (BS951) is used to make connections to gas and water pipes. It should not be removed under any circumstances.

PME

Sometimes, especially in country areas, the Electricity Company provides a different method of earthing the system, called 'protective multiple earth' (PME), by which earth-leakage current is fed back to the substation along the neutral return wire, and so to earth.

Regulations regarding the earthing of this system are particularly stringent. Cross-bonding cables to gas and water services are generally required to be larger with PME. Check this with your Electricity Company.

RCDs

Although the local Electricity Company normally provides effective earthing for the electrical system of your home, safe earthing is actually the consumer's own responsibility. With this in mind, it is worth installing a residual current device (RCD) into the house circuitry.

When conditions are normal, the current flowing out through the neutral conductor is exactly the same as that flowing in through the live one. Should there be an imbalance between the two caused by an earth leakage, the RCD will detect it immediately and isolate the circuitry.

An RCD can be either installed as a separate unit or incorporated into the consumer unit together with the main isolating switch.

A separate unit containing an RCD

RECOGNIZING AN OLD FUSE BOARD

Domestic wiring systems were once very different from the ones used today. Besides lighting, water-heating and cooker circuits, each socket outlet had its own circuit and fuse, while further circuits would usually be installed from time to time as the needs of the household changed. Consequently, an old house may have a mixture of 'fuse boxes' attached to a fuse board along with the meter. The wiring itself may be haphazard and badly labelled, with the serious danger that you may not safely isolate a circuit you're going to work on. Furthermore, you will not be able to tell whether a particular fuse is correctly and safely rated unless you know what type of circuit it is protecting.

If your home still has such an old-style fuse board, have it inspected and tested by a qualified electrician before you attempt to work on any part of the system. He or she can advise you as to whether your installation needs to be replaced with a modern consumer unit ; and if it is in good working condition, he or she can label the various circuits clearly to help you in the future.

An old-fashioned fuse board
This type of installation is out of date. A professional electrician may advise you to replace at least some of the components.

SEE ALSO

Details for:
Supplementary
bonding   10
RCDs   54

● **RCD**
An RCD – residual current device – is sometimes referred to as a residual current circuit breaker. It was formerly known as an ELCB – earth-leakage circuit breaker.

CONSUMER UNIT

SEE ALSO

Details for:	
Main switch equipment	16
RCD	17
Ring circuit	21

The consumer unit is the heart of your electrical installation, for every circuit in the house has to pass through it. There are several different types and styles of consumer unit, but all of them are based on similar principles.

Every consumer unit has a large main isolating switch, which can turn off the entire electrical system of the house. On some of the more-expensive units, the switch is in the form of an RCD that can be operated manually but will also 'trip' automatically should any serious fault occur, isolating the whole system in much less time than it would take for the Electricity Company's fuse to blow in a similar emergency.

Some consumer units are designed so that it is impossible to remove the outer cover without first turning off the main isolating switch. Even if yours is not of this type, you should always switch off before exposing any of the elements within the consumer unit.

Having turned off the main switch, remove the cover or covers so that you can see how the unit is arranged. The cover must be replaced before the unit is switched on again. Also, remember that even when the unit is switched off the cable connecting the meter to the main switch is still live – so take care.

Take note of the cables that feed the various circuits in the house. Ideally they should be spaced apart to prevent overheating. The black-insulated neutral wires run to a common neutral block where they are attached to their individual terminals. Similarly, the green-and-yellow earth wires run to a common earth block. The red-covered live conductors are connected to terminals on individual fuseways or circuit breakers.

Some wires will be twisted together in a single terminal. These are the two ends of a ring circuit, and that is how they should be wired.

CIRCUIT CABLES

FUSE CARRIER REMOVED
FROM BELL CIRCUIT

EARTH BLOCK

NEUTRAL BLOCK

OFF

SPARE FUSEWAY
(UNCONNECTED)

BELL CIRCUIT

LIGHTING CIRCUITS

IMMERSION-HEATER
CIRCUIT

RING CIRCUITS

MAIN SWITCH

COOKER CIRCUIT

METER LEADS

EARTH LEAD

A typical cartridge-fuse consumer unit
Your consumer unit may have different circuits.

In the consumer unit there is a fuseway for each circuit. Into the fuseway is plugged a fuse carrier, which is essentially a bridge between the main switch and that particular circuit. When the fuse carrier is removed from the consumer unit, the current cannot pass across the gap.

Identifying a fuse

Pull any of the fuse carriers out of the unit to see what kind of fuse it contains. At each end of the carrier you will see a single-bladed or double-bladed contact. A rewirable carrier will have a thin wire running from one contact to the other, held by a screw terminal at each end. Fuse wire is available in various thicknesses, carefully calculated to melt at given currents when a circuit is substantially overloaded, thus breaking the 'bridge' and isolating the circuit. Alternatively, the carrier may contain a

cartridge fuse similar to those used in 13amp plugs, though circuit fuses are larger, varying in size according to their rating. The cartridge is a ceramic tube containing a fuse wire packed in fine sand. The wire is connected to metal caps at the ends of the cartridge that snap into spring clips on the contacts of the fuse carrier. Cartridge fuses provide better protection since they blow faster than ordinary fuse wire; it is therefore advisable to use cartridge-fuse carriers wherever possible.

Fuse ratings

Whatever the type of fuses used in the consumer unit, they are rated in the same way. Cartridge fuses are colour-coded and marked with the appropriate amp rating for a certain type of circuit. Fuse wire is bought wrapped round a card which is clearly labelled.

Never insert fuse wire that is heavier than the gauge intended for the circuit. To do so could result in a dangerous fault going unnoticed because the fuse wire fails to melt. And it is even more dangerous to substitute any other type

of wire or metal strip; these provide no protection at all.

When you need to change a fuse, do not automatically replace it with one of the same rating. Check first that it is the correct type of fuse for the circuit. The fuse carrier should be marked and/or colour-coded. You can also look at the list of circuits printed on the inside of the consumer-unit cover to identify the carriers and their required ratings.

Keep spare fuse wire or cartridge fuses in or close to the consumer unit.

FUSE RATINGS		
Circuit	**Fuse**	**Colour coding**
Doorbell	5amp	White
Lighting	5amp	White
Immersion heater	15amp	Blue
Storage heater	15amp	Blue
Radial circuits – 20sq m maximum floor area 50sq m maximum floor area	20amp 30amp	Yellow Red
Ring circuits – 100sq m maximum floor area	30amp	Red
Shower unit	45amp	Green
Cooker	30amp	Red

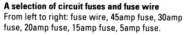

fuse wire
ref. 480

5 AMP
For lights and small plug circuits

15 AMP
For large plug circuits

30 AMP
For cookers and ring mains

A selection of circuit fuses and fuse wire
From left to right: fuse wire, 45amp fuse, 30amp fuse, 20amp fuse, 15amp fuse, 5amp fuse.

FUSE CARRIERS AND MCBs

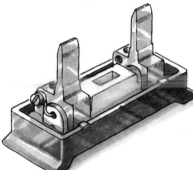

Single-bladed carrier with wire fuse

Double-bladed carrier with wire fuse

Cartridge-fuse carrier

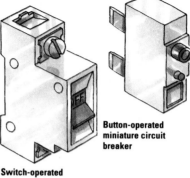

Button-operated miniature circuit breaker

Switch-operated miniature circuit breaker

SEE ALSO

Details for:
Circuit breakers	20
Circuit lengths	58

● **MCB ratings**
In order to conform to European standards, MCB ratings tend to vary slightly from circuit-fuse ratings. (See CIRCUITS: MAXIMUM LENGTHS.) However, it is perfectly acceptable if you have MCBs that match the slightly smaller ratings shown for circuit fuses.

● **Selecting miniature circuit breakers**
Instead of fuses, MCBs (miniature circuit breakers) are sometimes used to protect circuits. There are many types of MCB on the market, but only buy ones that are made to the required standards of construction and safety. Make sure that any MCB you use is marked BS 3871 (this is the relevant British Standard). There are also different classes of MCB, so look for Type 2 or Type B. And lastly, MCBs are classified according to the largest potential fault current they can clear; ask for M6 or M9, as these will clear any potential current likely to be met in a domestic situation. If for any reason these MCBs are unavailable, ask your Electricity Company if they will accept alternatives.

19

CHANGING A FUSE

SEE ALSO

Details for:	
Consumer unit	18
Fuses/ratings	19
Circuit breakers	19, 20

When everything on a circuit stops working, first of all check the fuse to see if it has blown. Turn off the main switch on the consumer unit, take off the cover and look for the failed fuse. To identify the fuse, look at the list of circuits inside the cover. If there is no list, inspect the most likely circuits. If, for example, the lights blew when you switched them on, you need check only the lighting circuits, which are usually colour-coded white.

Using a continuity tester
You can check a suspect cartridge fuse with a continuity tester. Place one of the tester's probes on each of the fuse's metal caps and then press the appropriate circuit-test button. If the bulb of the tester doesn't illuminate, the fuse has blown.

Checking a cartridge fuse

The simplest way to check a suspect cartridge fuse is to replace it with a new one and see if the circuit works. Alternatively, you can check the fuse with a metal-cased torch. Remove the bottom cap of the torch and touch one end of the fuse to the base of the battery while resting its other end against the battery's metal casing. If the torch bulb lights up, the fuse is sound.

Testing a cartridge fuse
With the torch switched on, hold the fuse against the battery and the metal casing.

Checking a rewirable fuse

On a blown rewirable fuse, a visual check will usually detect the broken wire and scorch marks on the fuse carrier. If you cannot see the whole length of the fuse wire, pull gently on each end of the wire with the tip of a small screwdriver to see if it's intact.

Pull the wire gently with a small screwdriver

HOW TO REPLACE FUSE WIRE

To replace blown fuse wire, loosen the two terminals holding the old wire and extract the broken pieces. Wrap one end of a new length of the correct type of fuse wire clockwise round one of the terminals and tighten the screw **(1)**. Then run the wire across to the other terminal, leaving it slightly slack, and attach it in the same way **(2)**. Cut off any excess wire from the ends.

If the wire passes through a tube in the fuse carrier, it has to be inserted before either terminal is tightened **(3)**.

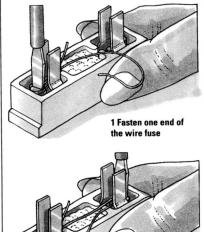

1 Fasten one end of the wire fuse

2 Wind the wire clockwise around the other terminal

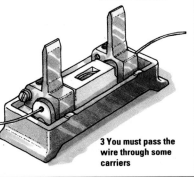

3 You must pass the wire through some carriers

IF THE FUSE BLOWS AGAIN

If a replaced fuse blows again as soon as the power is switched on, then there is either a fault or an overload (too many appliances plugged in) on that circuit and it must be detected and rectified before another fuse is inserted.

Miniature circuit breakers

In some consumer units you will find miniature circuit breakers (MCBs) instead of fuse carriers. Their current ratings tend to differ very slightly from fuse ratings, but the main difference is that circuit breakers switch to the 'off' position automatically, so a faulty circuit is obvious as soon as you inspect the consumer unit.

Turn the consumer unit's main switch off, then simply close the switch on the miniature circuit breaker to reset it. There is no fuse to replace. If the MCB switch or button will not stay in the 'on' position when power is restored, then there is still a fault on the circuit which must be rectified.

With the main switch off, reset the MCB

Checking out a fault

An electrician can test a circuit for you with special equipment, but first carry out some simple tests yourself.

Before inspecting any part of the circuit, turn off the consumer unit's main switch, remove the relevant fuse carrier or MCB, and keep it in your pocket so that no one can replace it while you are working.

Unplug all appliances on the faulty circuit to make sure that it is not simply overloaded, then switch on again. If the circuit is still faulty, switch off again and inspect the relevant socket outlets and light fittings to see if a conductor has worked loose and is touching one of the other wires or terminals or the outer casing, causing a short circuit.

If none of this enables you to find the fault, call in an electrician.

20

TYPES OF DOMESTIC ELECTRICAL CIRCUITS

Running from the consumer unit are the cables which supply the various fixed wiring circuits in your home. Not only are the sizes of the cables different; the circuits themselves also differ, depending on what they are used for and also, in some cases, how old they happen to be.

SEE ALSO	
Details for:	
Fuse ratings	19
Cables	22
Socket outlets	28
Fused connection units	34
Cooker circuit	37
Shower circuit	45
Circuits:	
maximum lengths	58

Ring circuits

The most common form of 'power' circuit for feeding socket outlets is the ring circuit, or 'ring main'. With this method of wiring, a cable starts from terminals in the consumer unit and goes round the house, connecting socket to socket and arriving back at the same terminals. This means that power can reach any of the socket outlets or fused connection units from both directions, which reduces the load on the cable.

Ring mains are always run in 2.5mm² cable and are protected by 30amp fuses or 32amp MCBs. Theoretically there is no limit to the number of socket outlets or fused connection units that can be fitted to one ring circuit provided that it does not serve a floor area of more than 100sq m (120sq yd) – a limit based on the number of heaters which would be adequate to warm that space. However, in practice two-storey houses usually have one ring main for the upper floor and another one for downstairs.

Spurs
The number of sockets on a ring main can be increased by adding extensions or 'spurs'. A spur can be either a single 2.5mm² cable connected to the terminals of an existing socket or fused connection unit or it can run from a junction box inserted in the ring.

It is good practice to have each spur serving one fused connection unit for a fixed appliance or one single or double socket outlet. You can have as many spurs on a ring circuit as there were sockets on it originally, and for this calculation a double socket is counted as two. The 30amp fuse that protects the ring main remains unchanged, no matter how many spurs are connected to the circuit.

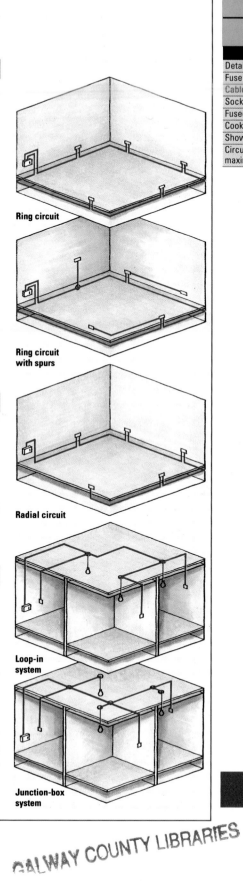

Ring circuit

**Ring circuit
with spurs**

Radial circuit

**Loop-in
system**

**Junction-box
system**

Radial circuits

A radial power circuit feeds a number of sockets or fused connection units but, unlike a ring circuit, its cable terminates at the last outlet. The size of cable and the fuse rating depend on the size of the floor area to be supplied by the circuit. In an area of up to 20sq m (24sq yd), the cable should be 2.5mm², protected by a 20amp MCB or a 20amp fuse of any type. For a larger area, up to 50sq m (60sq yd), you should use 4mm² cable with a 30amp cartridge fuse or 32amp MCB; a rewirable fuse is not permitted.

Any number of socket outlets can be supplied by one of these circuits, and spurs can be added if required. The circuits are known as multi-outlet radial circuits, but a powerful appliance such as a cooker or shower unit must have its own radial circuit.

Lighting circuits

Domestic lighting circuits are of the radial kind, but there are two systems currently in use.

The loop-in system simply has a single cable that runs from ceiling rose to ceiling rose, terminating at the last one on the circuit. Single cables also run from the ceiling roses to the various light switches.

The older system – known as the junction-box system – incorporates a junction box for each light. The boxes are situated conveniently on the single supply cable. A cable runs from each junction box to the ceiling rose, and another from the box to the light switch.

In practice, most lighting systems are a combination of the two methods.

A single circuit of 1mm² cable can serve the equivalent of twelve 100W light fittings. Check the load by adding together the wattage of all the light bulbs on the circuit. If it comes to more than 1200W, the circuit should be split. In any case, it makes sense to have two or more separate lighting circuits running from the consumer unit. If your house is large, requiring very long cable runs, use 1.5mm² two-core-and-earth cable instead of 1mm².

Lighting circuits must be protected by 5amp fuses or 6amp MCBs.

21

TYPES OF CABLE

SEE ALSO

Details for:	
Earth cable	16
Meter leads	16
Two-way lighting	52
Circuits:	
maximum lengths	58
Wire strippers	60

Two-core-and-earth cable

Cable for the fixed wiring of electrical systems normally has three conductors: the insulated live and neutral ones and the earth conductor lying between them, which is uninsulated except for the sheathing that encloses all three conductors. Cable up to 2.5mm^2 has solid single-core conductors; but larger sizes (up to 10mm^2) wouldn't be flexible enough if they had solid conductors, so each one is made up of seven strands. The live conductor is insulated with red

PVC, and the neutral one with black. If an earth conductor is exposed, as in a socket outlet, it should be covered with a green-and-yellow sleeve. You can buy sleeving from any electricians' supplier.

Heat-resistant sleeving is available for covering the conductors in an enclosed light fitting where the temperature could adversely affect the normal PVC insulation.

The PVC sheathing on the outside of the cable is usually white or grey.

Three-core-and-earth cable

This type of cable is used for a two-way lighting system, which can be turned on and off at different switches – at the top and bottom of a staircase, for example,

so that you never have to use the stairs in the dark. It contains three insulated conductors – with red, yellow and blue coverings – and a bare earth wire.

Single-core cable

Insulated single-core cable is used in buildings where the electrical wiring is run in metal or plastic conduit – a type of installation rarely found in domestic buildings. The cable is colour-coded in the normal way: red for live, black for neutral, and green-and-yellow for earth.

Single-core 16mm^2 cable insulated in

a green-and-yellow PVC covering is used for connecting the consumer unit to the earth. Single-core cable of the same size is used for connecting the consumer unit to the meter. The meter leads are insulated and sheathed in red for the live conductor and black for the neutral one.

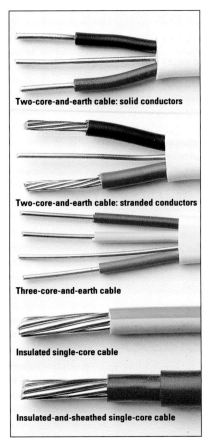

Two-core-and-earth cable: solid conductors

Two-core-and-earth cable: stranded conductors

Three-core-and-earth cable

Insulated single-core cable

Insulated-and-sheathed single-core cable

OLD CABLE

Houses which were wired before World War II may still have old cable that is sheathed and insulated in rubber, and some of them may even have old cable sheathed in lead.

Rubber sheathing is usually a matt black. It is more flexible than modern PVC insulation – unless it has deteriorated, in which case it will be crumbly.

This type of cable may be dangerous

STRIPPING CABLE

When cable is wired to an accessory, some of the sheathing and insulation must be removed.

Slit the sheathing lengthwise with a sharp knife, peel it off the conductors, then fold it over the blade and cut it off.

Take about 12mm (½in) of insulation off the ends of the conductors, using wire strippers.

Cover the uninsulated earth wire with a green-and-yellow plastic sleeve, leaving 12mm (½in) of the wire exposed for connecting to the earth terminal.

If more than one conductor is to be inserted in the same terminal, twist the exposed ends together with strong pliers to ensure the maximum contact for all of the wires.

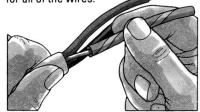

Slip colour-coded sleeving over the earth wire

● **Cable sizes**
The chart on the right gives the basic sizes of cables used for wiring domestic circuits. For details of the maximum permitted lengths for circuits, see CIRCUITS: MAXIMUM LENGTHS.

If the Company fuse is larger than 60amps, 25mm^2 meter leads are required, but consult your local Electricity Company for advice.

CIRCUIT-CABLE SIZES

Circuit	Size	Type
Fixed lighting	1.0mm^2 & 1.5mm^2	Two-core-and-earth
Bell or chime transformer	1.0mm^2	Two-core-and-earth
Immersion heater	2.5mm^2	Two-core-and-earth
Storage heater	2.5mm^2 & 4.0mm^2	Two-core-and-earth
Ring circuit	2.5mm^2	Two-core-and-earth
Spurs	2.5mm^2	Two-core-and-earth
Radial – 20amp	2.5mm^2	Two-core-and-earth
Radial – 30amp	4.0mm^2	Two-core-and-earth
Shower unit	10.0mm^2	Two-core-and-earth
Cooker	4.0mm^2 & 6.0mm^2	Two-core-and-earth
Consumer earth cable	16.0mm^2	Single core
Meter leads	16.0mm^2	Single core

CABLES
INSTALLING

RUNNING

CABLE

SEE ALSO
Details for:
Switching off 16
Nogging 61

INSIDE A HOLLOW WALL

To install a short cable run in a lath-and-plaster wall, hack the plaster away, fix the cable to the studs, and then plaster over again in the normal way.

Although you can run cable through the space between the two claddings of a stud partition wall, there is no way of doing this without some damage to the wall and the decoration. Drill a 12mm (½in) hole through the top wall plate above the spot where you are planning to position the switch, and then tap the wall directly below the hole to locate the nogging. Cut a hole in the lath-and-plaster to reveal the top of the nogging, then drill a similar hole through it.

Pass a lead weight on a plumb line through both of the holes and down to the location of the switch. Tie the cable to the line and pull it through.

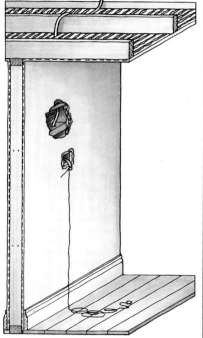

Running a cable through a hollow wall
If a nogging prevents you running cable directly to a switch, cut away some of the lath-and-plaster to drill a hole through the timber.

Long runs of cable are necessary to carry electricity from the consumer unit to all the sockets, light fittings and fixed appliances in the home. The cable must be fixed securely to the structure of the house along its route, except in confined spaces to which there is normally no access such as voids between floors and inside hollow walls. There are accepted ways of running and fixing cable, depending on particular circumstances.

Surface fixing

PVC-sheathed cable can be fixed to the surface of a wall or ceiling without any further protection. Fix it with plastic cable clips **(1)** or metal buckle clips **(2)** every 400mm (1ft 4in) on vertical runs, and every 250mm (10in) on horizontal runs. Try to keep the runs straight, and avoid kinks in the cable by keeping it

on the drum as long as possible. If you do have to remove kinks, pull the cable round a thick dowel held in a vice.

If a cable seems vulnerable, you can cover it with an impact-resistant plastic channel **(3)**. Having secured the cable with clips, you simply nail the channel in place over it.

1 Plastic cable clip

2 Metal buckle clip

Concealed fixing

While surface-fixed cable is acceptable in a cellar or in a garage or workshop, you wouldn't want to see it running across your living room walls or ceiling. From a decorative point of view it's better to bury it in the plaster or hide it in a wall void, and sheathed cable can be buried without further protection.

Where possible, run cable vertically to accessories such as switches or sockets, to avoid dangerous clashes with wall fixtures installed later. If that is not possible, you are permitted to run cable horizontally directly from the switch or socket. However, if a cable is not connected to a switch or socket on a wall in which it is concealed, then the cable must be within 150mm (6in) of the vertical or horizontal edges of the wall. Never, in any circumstances, run a buried cable diagonally across a wall.

Some people cover all buried cable

with a channel, but this isn't required by the IEE Wiring Regulations.

Cable that is buried in light plastic conduit can, if necessary, be withdrawn later without disturbing decorations, but the need very rarely arises in a house.

Mark out your cable runs on the plaster, making allowance for a 'chase' or channel about 25mm (1in) wide for single cable. Cut both sides with a bolster and club hammer, and then hack out the plaster between the cuts with a cold chisel. Normally, plaster is thick enough to conceal cable, but you may have to chop out some brickwork to get the depth. Clip the cable in the channel **(1)** and, when you have checked that the installation is working satisfactorily, plaster over it. To avoid electric shock, ensure that the power to that circuit is turned off before you use wet plaster round a switch or socket outlet **(2)**.

3 Impact-resistant plastic channel

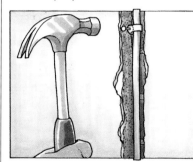

1 Nail plastic clips over the cable

2 Repair the plaster up to the switch

RUNNING
CABLE
UNDER FLOORS

SEE ALSO

Details for:	
Protective channel	23
Spur cables	31

Power and lighting circuits are often concealed beneath floors if access is possible. It isn't necessary to lift every floorboard to run a cable from one side of a room to the other: by lifting a board every 2m (6ft) or so, you should be able to pass the cable from one gap to the next with the help of a length of stiff wire bent into a hook at one end. Look for boards that have been taken up before, as they will be fairly easy to lift and you will therefore damage fewer boards.

Lifting floorboards

Lifting square-edged boards
Drive a wide bolster chisel between two boards about 50mm (2in) from the cut end of one of them (**1**). Lever that board up with the bolster, then do the same on its other edge, working along the board until you have raised it far enough to wedge a cold chisel under it (**2**). Proceed along the board, raising it with the chisel, till the board is loose.

Full-length boards
If you have to lift a board that runs the whole length of the floor from one skirting to the other, start somewhere near the middle of the board, close to

one of the floor joists. (The nail heads indicate the positions of joists.) Lever the board up and make a sawcut through it centred on the joist, then lift the board in the normal way.

Lifting tongue-and-groove boards
You cannot lift a tongue-and-groove floorboard until you have cut through the tongues along both sides of the board with a floorboard saw, which has a blade with a rounded tip.

Alternatively, use an electrician's 'skate', made with a cutting disc that fits between the boards. Run the tool back and forth with one foot.

Cutting a full-length board
Cut a full-length board in two directly over a floor joist.

Using a skate
Run the disc of an electrician's skate between tongue-and-groove boards.

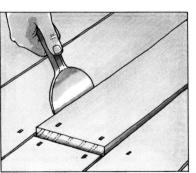

1 Prise up the floorboard with a bolster

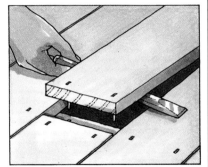

2 Wedge the raised end with a cold chisel

CUTTING A BOARD NEXT TO A SKIRTING

A joist that is fitted close to a wall may make it impossible to lift a floorboard in the normal way without damaging the bottom edge of the skirting.

In such a case, drill a starting hole through the floorboard alongside the joist, insert the blade of a padsaw in the hole, and cut across the board flush

with the side of the joist (**1**).

To support the cut end afterwards, nail a length of 50 x 50mm (2 x 2in) soft-wood to the joist. Hold the batten tightly against the undersides of the adjacent floorboards while you are fixing it, to ensure that the cut board will lie flush with the others (**2**).

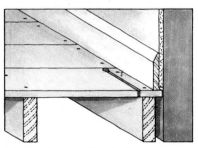

1 Cut through a trapped board with a saw

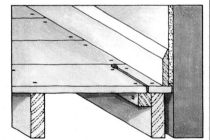

2 Support the cut board with a nailed batten

Solid floors

In a new concrete floor you can lay conduit and run cable through it before the concrete is poured.

In an existing solid floor you can cut a channel for conduit, although it's hard work without an electric hammer and chisel bit; and if the floor is tiled, you will not want to spoil it for one or two socket outlets. An alternative is to drop spur cables, buried in the wall plaster, from the ring circuit in the upper floor. Another way is to run cable through the wall from an adjacent area and channel it horizontally in the plaster just above the skirting. Yet another is to remove the skirting, clip the cable to the wall, and cover it with protective channel – but be sure to note the position of the cable, so you avoid piercing it when you nail back the skirting board.

In the roof space

In the roof space all wiring can be surface-run, but as people may enter it occasionally you must make sure that the cable is clipped securely to the joists or rafters. Run it through holes in the normal way, especially where joists are to be boarded over or in areas of access – around water tanks and near the entrance hatch, for example. If short lengths must run on top of a joist, add mechanical protection.

Wiring overlaid by roof-insulation material has a slightly higher chance of heating up. Lighting circuits do not present a problem, but circuits on which there are heaters, cookers or shower units, for example, are more critical. Wherever possible, run cable over thermal insulation. If you cannot avoid running it under the material, use a heavier cable, but consult a qualified electrician to be on the safe side.

When expanded-polystyrene insulation is in contact with electrical cable for a long time, it affects the plasticizer in the PVC sheathing on the cable. The plasticizer moves to the surface of the sheathing, reacts with the polystyrene, and forms a sticky substance on the cable. This becomes a dry crust which cracks if the cable is lifted out of the roof insulation and bent. It gives the impression that the cable insulation is cracking, but scientific testing has shown that the cracking is merely in the surface crust. On balance, however, it is best to keep cable away from polystyrene.

Running cable through the house structure

Use the most convenient method to run cable to sockets and switches.
1 Clip cable to battens nailed to roof timbers in the loft.
2 Junction boxes must be fixed securely.
3 Run cable through holes in the joists near the hatch.
4 Run cable over loft insulation.
5 To avoid damaging a finished floor, you can run a short spur through the wall from the next room.
6 When cable needs to run across the line of joists, drill holes 50mm (2in) below the joists' top edges.
7 When cable needs to run parallel to the joists, it can lie on the ceiling below.
8 Let cable drape onto the base below a suspended floor.
9 If it's impractical to run cable through a concrete floor, you can drop a spur from the floor above.

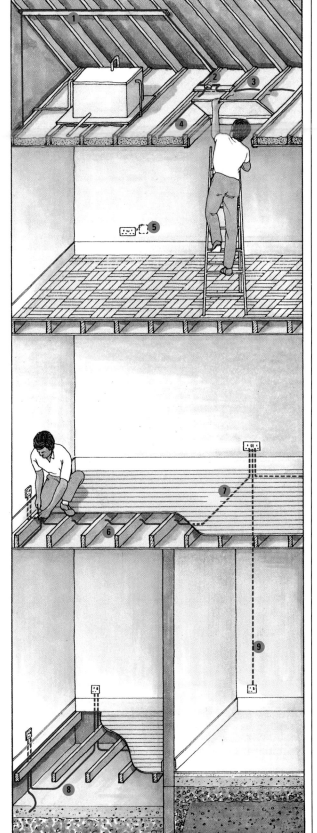

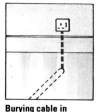

Burying cable in concrete
When you are laying a new concrete floor, take the opportunity to bury conduit for cable.

SEE ALSO

Details for:	
Cable clips	23
Concealing cable	23
Fitting a grommet	29
Running a spur	31

Running the cable

On the ground floor the cable can rest on the earth or on the concrete platform below the joists, providing there won't normally be access to the space. Allow enough slack, so that the cable is not suspended above the platform, which might put a strain on fixings to junction boxes or socket outlets. For the same reason, beside junction boxes or other accessories, secure cable with clips to the side of the joist. Never attach circuit cable to gas or water pipes; and don't run it next to heating pipes, as the heat could melt the insulation.

When laying cable between a floor and the ceiling below, it can rest on the ceiling without any other fixing provided it runs parallel with the joists. If it runs at right angles to the joists, drill a series of 12mm (½in) holes, one through each joist along the intended cable run. The holes must be at least 50mm (2in) below the tops of the joists, so that floorboard nails cannot at some time be hammered through the cable. Similarly holes must be at least 50mm (2in) from the bottom edge of ceiling joists, to be certain nails driven from below cannot pierce the cable. The space between the joists is limited, but you can cut down a spade bit and use it in a power drill.

Having marked out the position of a socket or fused connection unit, cut a channel from it down to the skirting board and, with an extra-long masonry drill in a power tool, remove the plaster from behind the skirting board. By using the drill at a shallow angle you can loosen much of the debris, but you will probably have to finish the job with a slim cold chisel. Raking the debris out from below with the same chisel also helps to dislodge it.

Pass a length of stiff wire with one end formed into a hook down behind the skirting board. Hook the cable and pull it through, at the same time feeding it from below with your other hand.

Preventing the spread of fire

Every time you cut an opening in the structure of the house for a cable, you are creating a potential route for fire to spread. After you have installed the cable, fill any holes between floors or rooms using plaster or some other non-flammable material (not asbestos). Even where you pass a cable into a mounting box you must fit a 'blind' grommet and cut a hole through it that is only just large enough for the cable.

Drilling the joists
Shorten a spade bit so that your drill fits between the joists.

Drilling behind skirting
Use an extra-long masonry drill to remove plaster behind a skirting board.

Fitting a grommet
There should be only just enough room for a cable to pass through a grommet into a mounting box for a switch or socket.

ASSESSING YOUR INSTALLATION

SEE ALSO

Details for:	
Switching off	16
Earth connection	16-17
Old fuse boxes	17
RCD	17
Fuse ratings	19
Replacing fuses	20
Old cable	22
Running cable	23–25
Replacing sockets	30
Converting radial circuit	33
Replacing switches	50

Inspect your electrical system to ensure that it is safe and adequate for your future needs. But remember, you should never examine any part of it without first switching off the power at the consumer unit.

If you are in doubt about any aspect of the installation, do not hesitate to ask a qualified electrician for an opinion. If you get in touch with your local Electricity Company, they will arrange for someone to test the whole system for you. There is usually a charge for this service.

QUESTIONS	ANSWERS
Do you have a modern consumer unit or a mixture of old 'fuse boxes'?	Old fuse boxes can be unsafe and should be replaced with a modern unit. Seek professional advice about this.
Is the consumer unit in good condition?	Replace a broken casing or cracked covers. Check that all the fuse carriers are intact and that they fit snugly in the fuseways.
Are the fuse carriers for the circuits clearly labelled?	If you cannot identify the various circuits, have an electrician test the system and label the fuses.
Are all your circuit fuses of the correct ratings?	Replace any fuses of the wrong rating. If an unusually large fuse is protecting one of the circuits, don't change it without getting professional advice – it may have a special purpose. Any wire other than proper fuse wire found in a fuse carrier should be replaced at once.
Are the cables that lead from the consumer unit in good condition?	The cables should be fixed securely, with no bare wires showing. If the cables appear to be insulated with rubber, have the whole installation checked as soon as possible. Rubber insulation has a limited life, so yours could already be dangerous.
Is the earth connection from the consumer unit intact and in good condition?	If the connection seems loose or corroded, have the Electricity Company check on whether the earthing is sound. You can check an RCD by pushing the test button to make sure it is working mechanically.
What is the condition of the fixed wiring between floors and in the loft or roof space?	If the cables are rubber-insulated, have the system checked by a professional, but first examine each of the circuits, as they may not all have been renewed at the same time. If cable is run in conduit, it can be hard to check on its condition – but if it looks doubtful where it enters accessories, have the circuit checked professionally. Wiring should be fixed securely and sheathing should run into all accessories, with no bare wire in sight. Junction boxes on lighting circuits should be screwed firmly to the structure and should have their covers in place.
Is the wiring discreet and orderly?	Tidy all surface-run wiring into straight properly-clipped runs. Better still, bury the cable in the wall plaster or run it under floors and inside hollow walls.
Are there any old round-pin socket outlets?	Make sure their wiring is adequate. Replace old radial circuits with modern wiring and 13amp square-pin sockets as soon as possible.
Are the outer casings of all accessories in good condition and fixed securely to the structure?	Replace any cracked or broken components and secure any loose fittings.
Do switches on all accessories work smoothly and effectively?	If the switches are not working properly, replace the accessories.
Are all the conductors inside accessories connected securely to their terminals?	Tighten all loose terminals and ensure that no bare wires are visible. Fit green-and-yellow sleeves to earth wires if they have not been fitted.

QUESTIONS	ANSWERS
Is insulation around wires inside any accessories dry and crumbly?	If so, it is rubber insulation in advanced decomposition. Replace the covers carefully and have a professional check the system as soon as possible.
Do any sockets, switches or plugs feel warm? Is there a burning smell, or scorch marks on sockets or around the base of plug pins? Does a socket outlet spark when you pull out a plug? Or a switch when you operate it?	These symptoms mean loose connections in the accessory or plug, or a poor connection between plug and socket. Tighten loose connections and clean all fuse clips, fuse caps and plug pins with silicon-carbide paper, then wipe them with a soft cloth. If the fault persists, try a new plug. If that fails to cure the problem, replace the socket or switch.
Is it difficult to insert a plug in a socket?	The socket is worn and should be replaced.
Are your sockets in the right places?	Sockets should be placed conveniently round a room so that you need never have long flexes trailing across the floor or under carpets. Add sockets to the ring circuit by running spurs.
Do you have enough sockets?	If you have to use plug adaptors, you need more sockets. Replace singles with doubles, add spurs, or extend the ring circuit.
Is there old braided twin flex hanging from some ceiling roses?	Replace it with PVC-insulated-and-sheathed flex. Also check that the wiring inside the rose is PVC-insulated.
Are there earth wires inside your ceiling roses?	If not, get professional advice on whether to replace the lighting circuits
Is your lighting efficient?	Make sure you have two-way switching on stairs, and consider extra sockets or different light fittings to make the lighting more effective or atmospheric.
Is there power in the garage or workshop?	Detached outbuildings need their own power supply.

SEE ALSO

Details for:

Flex	12
Replacing fuses	20
Replacing sockets	30
Running a spur	31
Extending ring circuit	32
Replacing switches	50
Two-way switching	52
Wiring outbuildings	56-57

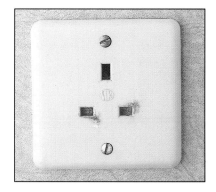

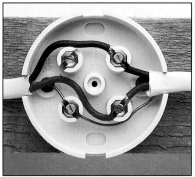

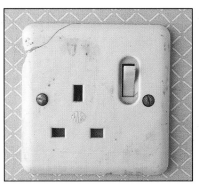

From left to right:

Scorch marks
Scorch marks on a socket or round the base of plug pins indicates poor connections.

Overloaded socket
If you have to use adaptors to power your appliances, you should fit extra sockets.

Unprotected connections
Sheath any bare earth wires and make sure covers or faceplates are fitted to all accessories.

From left to right:

Incorrect fuse
Replace improper wire with fuse wire.

Round-pin socket
Replace old round-pin sockets with 13amp square-pin sockets.

Damaged socket
Replace cracked or broken faceplates.

SEE ALSO

Details for:	
Switching off	16
Wiring a socket	30
Wiring kitchen appliances	36
Circuit lengths	58

Whatever the type of circuits in your home, use only standard 13amp square-pin sockets. All round-pin sockets are now out of date; and although they may not be actually dangerous at the moment, you should have them checked and consider changing your wiring to accommodate 13amp sockets.

Before you start work on any socket, switch the power off at the consumer unit and remove the fuse for the relevant circuit – then test the socket with an appliance that you know to be working, in order to make sure that the socket has been switched off properly.

TYPES OF 13AMP SOCKET

Although all sockets are functionally very similar, there are several variations of the basic component.

There are single and double sockets, and both are available either switched or unswitched and with or without neon indicators so you can see at a glance whether the socket is switched on. All of these are wired in the same way.

Another basic difference is in how the sockets are mounted. They can be surface-mounted (screwed to the wall in a plastic box) or flush-mounted in a metal box buried in the wall with only its faceplate visible.

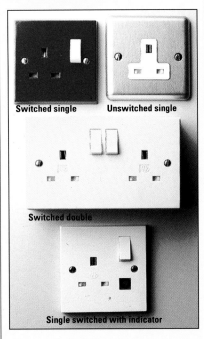

Triple sockets
Triple sockets are useful where several electrical appliances are grouped together.

Switched single   **Unswitched single**

Switched double

Single switched with indicator

Choose the most convenient positions for television, hi-fi, table lamps and so on, and position your socket outlets accordingly. To avoid using adaptors or long leads, distribute the sockets evenly round living rooms and bedrooms, and wherever possible fit doubles rather than singles. Don't forget sockets for running the vacuum cleaner in hallways and on landings.

The optimum height for a socket is 225 to 300mm (9in to 1ft) above the floor. This will clear most skirting boards and leave ample room for flexible cord (flex) to hang from a plug, but is high enough not to be in danger of getting struck by the vacuum cleaner.

In the kitchen, fit at least four double sockets 150mm (6in) above the work-tops, or more if you have a lot of small appliances. In addition, fit sockets for floor-standing appliances such as your refrigerator and dishwasher.

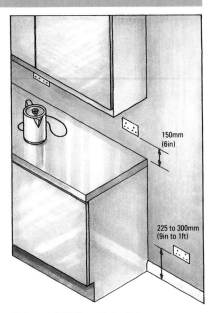

150mm (6in)

225 to 300mm (9in to 1ft)

Optimum heights for socket outlets

Surface-mounting socket outlets

First break out the thin plastic webs that cover the fixing holes in the back of a plastic mounting box. The best tool to use for this is an electrician's screwdriver. Two fixings should be sufficient. The fixing holes are slotted to enable easy adjustment.

Hold the mounting box firmly against a masonry wall, levelling it at the same time with a small spirit level, and mark the position of the fixing holes on the wall with a bradawl through the holes in the back of the box. Drill and plug the holes with No 8 wall plugs.

With a larger screwdriver and pliers, break out the plastic web covering the most convenient cable-entry hole in the box. For surface-run cable this will be in the side; for buried cable it will be the one in the base.

Feed the cable into the mounting box to form a loop about 75mm (3in) long **(1)**, and then fix the box to the wall with 32mm (1¼in) countersunk woodscrews. Finally, wire and fit the socket.

Fixing to a hollow wall
On a dry-partition or lath-and-plaster wall, a surface-mounted box is fixed with any of the standard fixings used for hollow walls. Alternatively, use ordinary woodscrews if you are able to position the box over a stud – in which case, make sure you can feed the cable into the mounting box past the stud **(2)**.

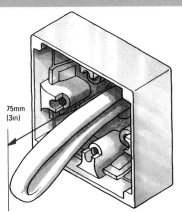

75mm (3in)

1 Leave a 75mm (3in) loop of cable at the box

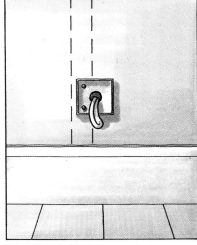

2 Feed the cable into the box past the stud

Fixing to masonry

Hold the metal box against the wall and draw round it with a pencil (**1**), then mark a 'chase' (channel) running up from the skirting to the box's outline.

Using a bolster or a cold chisel, cut away the plaster, down to the brickwork (**2**), within the marked area.

With a masonry drill, bore several rows of holes down to the required depth (**3**) across the recess for the box, then with a cold chisel cut away the brick to the depth of the holes so that the box will lie flush with the plaster.

Try the box in the recess. If it fits in snugly, mark the wall through the fixing holes in its back, then drill the wall for the screw plugs. If you have made the recess too deep or the box rocks from side to side, apply some filler in the recess and press the box into it, flush with the wall and properly positioned. After about 10 minutes ease the box out carefully and leave the filler to harden so that you can mark, drill and plug the fixing holes through it.

Knock one or more of the blanked-off holes in the box out to accommodate the cable. Fit a grommet into each hole to protect the cable's sheathing from the metal edges (**4**), feed the cable into the box, and screw the box to the wall.

Plaster up to the box and over the cable chased into the wall; then, when the plaster has hardened, wire and fit the socket itself.

Fixing to plasterboard

In order to fit a flush socket to a wall made of plasterboard over wooden studs, trace the outline of the metal box in position on the wall and drill a hole in each corner of the outline. Then cut out the recess for the box with a padsaw.

Punch out the blanked-off entry holes in the box and fit rubber grommets, then feed the cable into the box.

Clip dry-wall fixing flanges to the sides of the box (**5**). These will hold it in place by gripping the wall from inside. Ease one side of the box, with flange, into the recess; and then, holding the screw-fixing lugs so as not to lose the box, manoeuvre it until both flanges are behind the plasterboard and the box sits snugly in the hole. (See also right.)

Finally, wire and fit the socket. As you tighten up the fixing screws, the plasterboard will be gripped between the flanges and the faceplate.

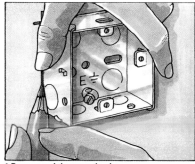

1 Draw round the mounting box

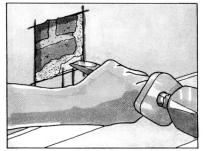

2 Chop away the plaster with a cold chisel

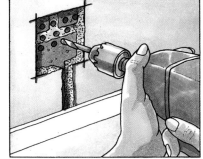

3 Drill out the brickwork with a masonry bit

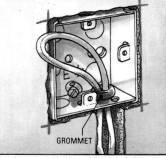

GROMMET

4 Fit a soft grommet in the cable-entry hole

5 Dry-wall fixing flanges clipped to a box

FLUSH MOUNTING TO LATH-AND-PLASTER

If you want to fit a flush socket outlet in a lath-and-plaster wall, try to locate it over a stud or nogging.

Mark the position of the metal box, cut out the plaster, and saw away the laths with a padsaw. Try the box for fit, and if necessary chop a notch in the woodwork until the box lies flush with the wall surface (**1**). Feed in the cable, and screw the box to the stud before wiring and fitting the socket.

If you cannot position the socket on a stud, cut away enough plaster and laths to make a slot in the wall running from one stud to the next. Between the studs, screw or skew-nail a softwood nogging to which you can fix the box. If necessary, set the batten back from the front edges of the studs, in order to make the box lie flush with the wall surface (**2**). Feed the cable into the box and make good the surrounding plaster before you wire and fit the socket.

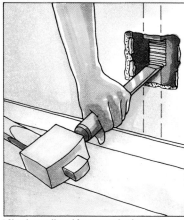

1 Notch a wall stud for a mounting box

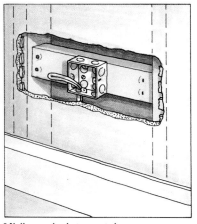

2 Nail a nogging between studs
Cut away wall plaster and laths when you have to fix a mounting box between wall studs.

SEE ALSO

Details for:	
Running a cable	23-25
Wiring a socket	30

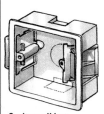

Cavity-wall box
Instead of fitting dry-wall fixing flanges to a standard mounting box, you can use a special cavity-wall box with integral hinged flanges that you push through the sides of the box after it is fitted.

REPLACING SOCKET OUTLETS

SEE ALSO

Details for:

Switching off	16
Stripping cable	22
Types of socket	28
Mounting to a hollow wall	29
Recessing metal box	29

If you need to replace a broken or faulty socket outlet, there are several options worth considering before you embark on the job.

Simple replacement

Replacing a damaged socket with a similar one is a fairly straightforward job. A socket of any style will fit a metal mounting box, but check carefully when you substitute a socket that screws to a surface-mounted plastic box. Although it will fit and function perfectly well, square corners and edges on either will not suit rounded ones on the other. In such a case you may also have to buy a new, matching box.

An unswitched socket outlet can be replaced with a switched one without any change to the wiring or fixing.

Switch off the power at the consumer unit and take out the circuit fuse, then remove the fixing screws from the face-plate and pull the socket out of the box.

Loosen the terminals to free the conductors. Check that all is well inside the box, then connect the conductors to the terminals of the new socket. Fit the faceplate, using the original screws if those supplied with the new socket don't match the thread in the box.

Surface to flush

If you have to renew a socket, you may want to take the opportunity to replace a surface-mounted box with a flush one.

Turn off the power, remove the old socket and box, and then recess the new metal box into the wall, taking care not to damage the cable.

Replacing a single socket with a double

One way to increase the number of socket outlets in a room is to substitute doubles for singles. Any single socket on a ring circuit can be replaced with a double without making any changes to the wiring. Similarly, you can replace a single socket on a spur with a double socket outlet. Consider using switched sockets; they are safer than unswitched ones and the wiring is identical.

Surface to surface

Replacing a surface-mounted single socket with a surface-mounted double is quite easy. Having removed the old socket, simply fix the new, double box to the wall in the same place.

Flush to surface

Although flush-mounted socket outlets are neater, you may want to avoid the disturbance to decor that's involved in installing a double one. Instead, you can fit a double surface-mounted socket over the buried box of a single one (1). Switch off the power and remove the socket, leaving the metal box and the wiring in place, then knock out the cable-entry hole in the double plastic box and feed the cable through it. When the plastic box is centred over the old metal one, two fixing holes will line up with the fixing lugs on the buried box. Break out the plastic webs and fix the new box to the lugs with the screws that held the old socket in place. Wire up the new double socket and fit it.

Flush to flush

Switch off the power to the circuit, and remove the old single socket and its metal box. Then try the new double box over the hole. You can centre the box over the hole or align it with one end (2), whichever is more convenient. Trace the outline of the box on the wall and cut out the brickwork.

Use a similar procedure to substitute a double socket for a single one in a hollow wall, installing the socket by whichever method is most convenient.

Surface to flush

To replace a single surface-mounted socket with a flush double, cut a recess for the metal box in the normal way.

CONNECTING UP TO A SOCKET

When a single cable is involved, strip off the sheathing in the normal way and connect the wires to the terminals: the black wire to neutral – N, the red one to live – L, and the earth wire, which you should insulate yourself with a sleeve, to earth – E (1). If necessary, fold the stripped ends over so that no bare wire protrudes from a terminal.

When connecting to a ring circuit, cut through the loop of cable, strip the sheathing from each half and twist together the bared ends of matching wires – live with live and so on – after slipping sleeves on the earth wires (2).

Cable is stiff, and can make it difficult to close the socket faceplate, so bend each conductor until it folds into the mounting box. Locate both fixing screws and tighten them gradually in turn until the plate fits firmly in place against the wall or box.

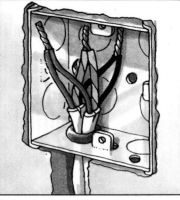

1 Wiring a socket outlet

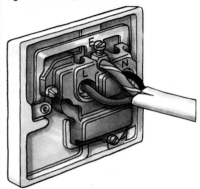

2 Twist cut wires together

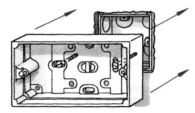

1 Fixing a surface-mounted box over a flush one

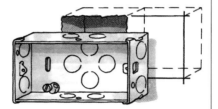

2 Cut out extra brickwork for a double box

If you need more sockets in a room, you can run 2.5mm² spur cables from a ring circuit and have as many spurs as there are sockets already on the ring. A spur can feed one single or one double socket.

A spur cable can be connected to any socket or fused connection unit on the ring circuit, or to a new junction box inserted in the circuit. If running a spur cable from an existing socket would mean disturbing the plaster, it will be more convenient to use a junction box. And if there is no socket outlet within easy reach of the proposed new one, using a junction box may save cable.

If the cable is surface-run and you want to extend a row of sockets – behind a workbench, for example – then it will be simpler to connect the spur to a socket.

Examine the socket. If it is fed by a single cable, it is probably already on a spur; and if there are three cables in the socket, then it's already feeding a spur itself. What you need to look for is a socket that has two cables.

SEE ALSO	
Details for:	
Switching off	16
Cables	22
Stripping cable	22
Running cable	23-25

Connecting to an existing socket

Fix the new socket, then wire it up in the normal way (see opposite) and run its spur cable to the existing socket outlet. Switch off the electricity and remove the existing socket. You may have to enlarge the entry hole or knock out another one to take the spur cable. Feed the cable into the box, prepare the conductors, and twist their bared ends together with those of the matching conductors of the ring circuit. Insert the wires in their terminals (red – L; black – N; and green-and-yellow – E) and replace the socket. Then switch the power on and test the new socket.

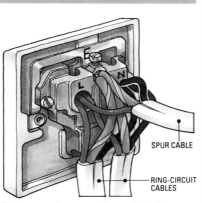

Taking a spur from an existing socket outlet

SPUR CABLE

RING-CIRCUIT CABLES

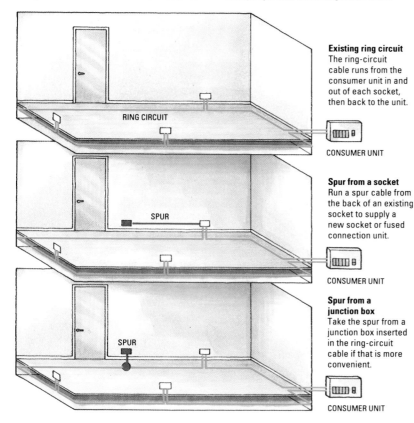

RING CIRCUIT

CONSUMER UNIT

Existing ring circuit
The ring-circuit cable runs from the consumer unit in and out of each socket, then back to the unit.

SPUR

CONSUMER UNIT

Spur from a socket
Run a spur cable from the back of an existing socket to supply a new socket or fused connection unit.

SPUR

CONSUMER UNIT

Spur from a junction box
Take the spur from a junction box inserted in the ring-circuit cable if that is more convenient.

CONNECTING TO A JUNCTION BOX

You will need a 30amp junction box with three terminals to connect to a ring circuit. It will have either knock-out cable-entry holes or a special cover that rotates to blank off unneeded holes. The cover must be screw-fixed.

Lift a floorboard close to the new socket, where you can connect to the ring-circuit cable without stretching it.

Fix a platform for the box by nailing battens near the bottoms of two joists (see right) and screwing a 100 x 25mm (4 x 1in) strip of wood between the joists and resting on the battens. Loop the ring-circuit cable over the platform before fixing it, so that the cable need not be cut for connecting up. Remove the cover, screw the junction box to the platform, and break out two cable-entry holes. If you do forget to loop the cable over the platform, simply cut the cable when you come to connect it up.

Turn off the power at the consumer unit, then rest the ring-circuit cable across the box and mark the amount of sheathing to remove. Slit it lengthwise and peel it off the conductors. Don't cut the live and neutral conductors, but slice away just enough insulation on each to expose a section of bare wire that will fit into a terminal (see right). Cut the earth wire and fit insulating sleeves on the two ends.

Remove the screws from all three of the terminals and lay the wires across them – with the earth wire in the middle terminal, and the live and neutral ones on each side. Push the wires home with a screwdriver.

Having fitted and wired the new spur socket, run its cable to the junction box. Cut and prepare the ends of the wires, and break out an entry hole so that the spur wires can be fitted to the terminals of the box (see right). Take care that only colour-matched wires from both cables share terminals.

Replace the fixing screws, starting them by hand as they are easily cross-threaded, then tighten them up with a screwdriver. Check that all of the wires are secured and that the cables all fit snugly in their entry holes, with the sheathing running into the box, then fit the cover on the box.

Fix each cable to a nearby joist with cable clips, to take the strain off the terminals, then replace the floorboards.

Switch the power back on and test the new socket.

Make a wooden platform for a junction box

RING-CIRCUIT CABLE

SPUR CABLE

RING-CIRCUIT CABLE

Taking a spur from a junction box

31

SEE ALSO

Details for:	
Switching off	16
Ring-circuit Regulations	21
Running cable	23-25
Positioning sockets	28
Mounting boxes	28-29
Wiring sockets	30
Junction box	31
Circuit lengths	58

There are times when it is better to extend a ring circuit than to fit spurs. For example, if you want to wire a room that isn't adequately serviced, or all of the conveniently placed sockets already have spurs running from them. You can break into the ring at an existing socket or via junction boxes. Either way, switch off the power to the circuit before you break into it.

Using an existing socket

Disconnect one in-going cable from a socket on the ring circuit and take it to the first new socket. Do this via a junction box if the cable won't otherwise reach. Continue the extension with a new section of cable from socket to socket, finally running it from the last new one back to the socket where you broke into the ring. Joining the new cable to the old one within the socket completes the circuit.

Using junction boxes

Cut the ring cable and connect each cut end to a junction box, then run a new length of cable from one box to the other, looping it into the new sockets.

Running the extension

No matter how you plan to break into the ring, always install the new cable first and then connect it up to the circuit at the last moment. This allows you to use power tools to run the extension – but don't forget to switch the power off just before connecting up.

Decide positions for the new sockets and plan your cable run (an easy route is better than a shorter, more difficult one). Allow some slack in the cable.

Cut out the plaster and brickwork for sockets and cable, then fit the boxes for the sockets. Now run the cable, leaving enough spare for joining to the ring circuit, and take it up behind the skirting to the first socket. Leave a loop hanging near the box (see right), then take the cable on to the next one, and so on until all the new sockets are supplied. Take the excess cable on to the point where you plan to join the ring.

Fit the new sockets, then switch off the electricity, break into the ring, and connect the extension to it. Switch the power on and test all the new sockets separately. Make good the plasterwork.

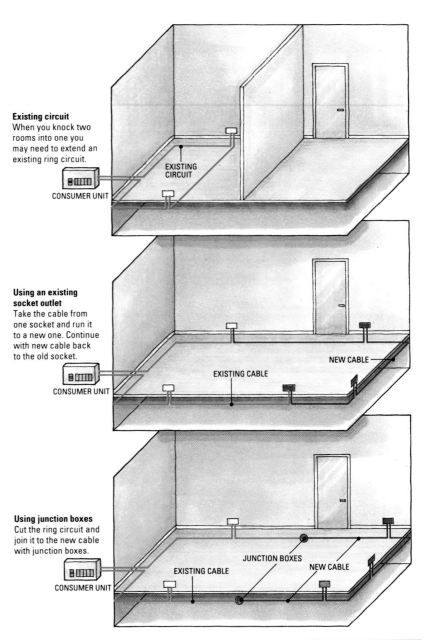

Existing circuit
When you knock two rooms into one you may need to extend an existing ring circuit.

EXISTING CIRCUIT

CONSUMER UNIT

Using an existing socket outlet
Take the cable from one socket and run it to a new one. Continue with new cable back to the old socket.

NEW CABLE

EXISTING CABLE

CONSUMER UNIT

Using junction boxes
Cut the ring circuit and join it to the new cable with junction boxes.

JUNCTION BOXES

NEW CABLE

EXISTING CABLE

CONSUMER UNIT

LEAVE SOME SLACK IN THE CIRCUIT

Don't pull the cable too tight when you are running a new circuit. It places a strain on the connections and makes it difficult to modify the circuit at a later stage, should that become necessary.

Leave a generous loop of cable at each of the new socket positions till you have run the complete circuit. At that stage you can pull the loop back ready for connecting to the socket.

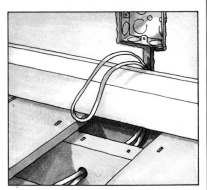

Leave ample cable above the skirting

CONVERTING A RADIAL CIRCUIT

SEE ALSO	
Details for:	
Switching off	16
Consumer unit	18
Fuse ratings	19
Radial-circuit Regulations	21
Cable	22
Running cable	23-25
Positioning sockets	28
Wiring sockets	30
Circuit lengths	58
Continuity tester	60

If you have a radial circuit, you may want to convert it to a ring circuit, particularly if you wish to supply a larger area. Before starting work, switch off at the consumer unit.

Checking cable and fuse

If the radial circuit is wired with $2.5mm^2$ cable (solid conductors), continue the circuit back to the consumer unit with the same size cable, but substitute a 30amp fuse and fuseway in place of the 20amp fuse. Even if the circuit is wired with $4mm^2$ cable (stranded conductors), you can complete the ring with $2.5mm^2$ cable. Check there's a 30amp fuse. See also CIRCUITS: MAXIMUM LENGTHS.

The extra cable is run in exactly the same way as described for extending a ring circuit (see opposite). Join the new cable at the last socket on the radial circuit and run it to all the new sockets. From the last socket, run the cable to the consumer unit.

Connecting to the consumer unit

You should examine your consumer unit and familiarize yourself with it. Even when the unit is switched off, the cable that connects the meter to the main switch is still live – so take great care. First locate the terminals to which the radial circuit is connected. The live (red wire) terminal is on the fuseway (or MCB) from which you removed the circuit fuse prior to starting work. The neutral (black wire) terminal is on the neutral block, to which all of the black wires are connected. You can usually trace the black wire you are looking for by working along from the sheathed part of the cable – and the earth terminal similarly, by tracing the green-and-yellow-insulated conductor. Pass the new cable into the consumer unit close to the original radial-circuit cable. Cut it to length, strip off the sheathing and prepare the conductors.

Disconnect the live (red) conductor from its terminal and, having checked for continuity (see far right), twist its end together with that of the red wire from the new cable, then reconnect both conductors in the same terminal. Do the same for the black wires and then the green-and-yellow ones – but slip a sleeve over the new earth wire.

Check that the circuit fuse is of the correct rating, then replace the fuse carrier. Close the consumer unit, switch on the power, and test the circuit.

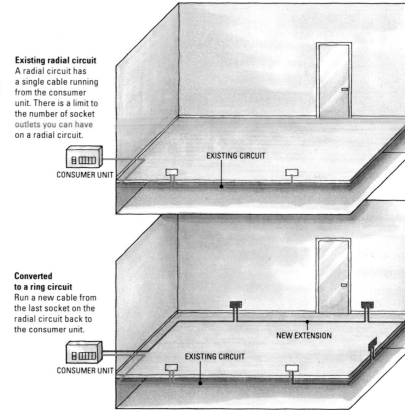

Existing radial circuit
A radial circuit has a single cable running from the consumer unit. There is a limit to the number of socket outlets you can have on a radial circuit.

CONSUMER UNIT

EXISTING CIRCUIT

Converted to a ring circuit
Run a new cable from the last socket on the radial circuit back to the consumer unit.

NEW EXTENSION

EXISTING CIRCUIT

CONSUMER UNIT

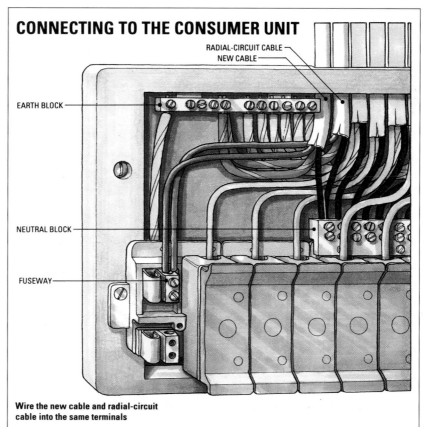

CONNECTING TO THE CONSUMER UNIT

RADIAL-CIRCUIT CABLE
NEW CABLE

EARTH BLOCK

NEUTRAL BLOCK

FUSEWAY

Wire the new cable and radial-circuit cable into the same terminals

● **Testing for continuity**
Check the continuity of the new ring circuit before you twist the conductors together and connect them to their terminals in the consumer unit. Using a continuity tester, place one of its probes on the red conductor at one end of the circuit cable and its other probe on the red conductor at the other end. Press the tool's test button and, if the circuit is complete, the tester's light will illuminate. Carry out the same test for the black conductors and then the earth wires.

FIXED
APPLIANCES

SEE ALSO

Details for:	
Stripping flex	13
Switching off	16
Power circuits	21
Stripping cables	22
Mounting boxes	28-29

13amp sockets are designed to enable appliances to be moved from room to room, with one socket used for different appliances at different times. But many electrical appliances, both large and small, are fixed to the structure of the house, or stand in one position permanently. Such appliances may therefore just as well be wired into your electrical installation permanently. For some there is no alternative, and they may even require radial circuits of their own direct from the consumer unit.

Changing a fuse
With the electricity turned off, remove the retaining screw in the face of the fuse holder. Take the holder from the connection unit; prise out the old fuse and fit a new one; then replace the holder and the retaining screw.

FUSED CONNECTION UNITS

A fused connection unit is basically a device for joining the flex (or sometimes cable) of an appliance to circuit wiring. The connection unit incorporates the added protection of a cartridge fuse similar to that found in a 13amp plug. If the appliance is connected by a flex, choose a unit that has a cord outlet in the faceplate.

Some fused connection units are fitted with a switch, and some of these have a neon indicator that shows at a glance whether they are switched on. A switched connection unit allows you to isolate the appliance from the mains.

All fused connection units are single (there are no double versions available) with square faceplates that fit metal boxes for flush mounting or standard surface-mounted plastic boxes.

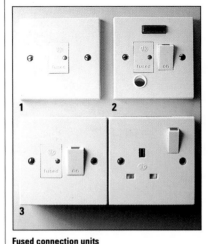

Fused connection units
1 Unswitched connection unit.
2 Switched unit with cord outlet and indicator.
3 Connection unit and socket outlet in a dual mounting box.

Small appliances

Small permanent electrical appliances with ratings of up to 3000W (3kW) – wall heaters, cooker hoods, heated towel rails and so on – can be wired into a ring or radial circuit by means of fused connection units.

Although such appliances could be connected by means of 13amp plugs to socket outlets, the electrical contact would not be so good – and there is also some risk of fire with that type of permanent installation.

Before wiring a fused connection unit to the house circuitry, always remember to switch off the power at the consumer unit.

Mounting a fused connection unit

A fused connection unit is mounted in the same type of box as an ordinary socket outlet, and the box is fixed to the wall in exactly the same way. The unit can also be mounted in a dual box that is designed to hold two single units – for example, a standard socket outlet beside a connection unit. The socket is wired to the ring circuit, and the two units are linked together inside the box by a short 2.5mm^2 spur.

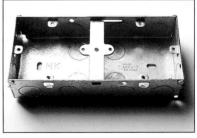

A dual mounting box

Wiring a fused connection unit

Fused connection units can be supplied by a ring circuit, a radial circuit or a spur. Some appliances are connected to the unit with flex, others with cable. Either way, the wiring arrangements inside the units are the same. Units with cord outlets have clamps to secure the connecting flex.

An unswitched connection unit has two live (L) terminals, one marked 'Load' for the brown wire of the flex, and the other marked 'Mains' for the red wire from the circuit cable. The blue wire from the flex and the black wire from the circuit cable go to similar neutral (N) terminals; and both earth wires are connected to the unit's earth (E) terminal or terminals (**1**).

Switched connection unit
A fused connection unit with a switch also has two sets of terminals. Those marked 'Mains' are for the spur or ring cable that supplies the power; the terminals marked 'Load' are for the flex or cable from the appliance.

Wire up the flex side first, connecting the brown wire to the L terminal and the blue one to the N terminal, both on the 'Load' side. Connect the green-and-yellow wire to the E terminal (**2**) and tighten the cord clamp.

Attach the circuit conductors to the 'Mains' terminals – red to L and black to N, then sleeve the earth wire and take it to the E terminal (**2**).

If the fused connection unit is on a ring circuit, you must fit two circuit conductors into each 'Mains' terminal and the earth terminal. Before securing the unit in its box with the fixing screws, make sure the wires are held firmly in the terminals and can fold away neatly.

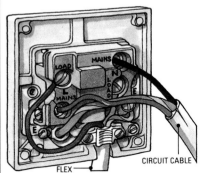

1 Wiring a fused connection unit

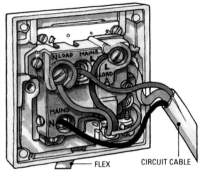

2 Wiring a switched fused connection unit

WIRING
HEATERS

When installing a skirting heater, wall-mounted heater or oil-filled radiator, wire the appliance to a fused connection unit mounted nearby at a height of about 150 to 300mm (6in to 1ft) from the floor. Whether the connection to the unit is by flex or cable will depend on the type of appliance. Follow the manufacturer's instructions for wiring, and fit the appropriate fuse in the connection unit.

In a bathroom, a fused connection unit must be mounted out of reach. Any heater that is mounted near the floor of a bathroom must therefore be wired to a connection unit installed outside the room. If the appliance is fitted with flex, mount a flexible-cord outlet (1) next to the appliance – and then run a cable from the outlet to the fused connection unit outside the bathroom and connect it to the 'Load' terminals in the unit.

The flexible-cord outlet is mounted on a standard surface-mounted box or flush on a metal box. At the back of the faceplate are three pairs of terminals to take the conductors from the flex and the cable (2).

Radiant wall heaters for use in bathrooms must be fixed high on the wall, out of reach from the bath or shower. A fused connection unit fitted with a 13amp fuse (or a 5amp fuse for a heater of 1kW or less) must be mounted at the same level, and the heater must be controlled by a double-pole pull-cord switch (the type that works by breaking both live and neutral contacts). Many heaters have a built-in double-pole switch; otherwise you must fit a ceiling-mounted 15amp double-pole switch between the fused connection unit and the heater. Switch terminals marked 'Mains' are for the cable on the circuit side of the switch; those marked 'Load' are for the heater side. The earth wires are connected to a common terminal on the switch box.

If it is not possible to run a spur to the fused connection unit from a socket outside the bathroom, don't be tempted to connect a radiant wall heater to the lighting circuit. Instead, run a separate radial circuit from the connection unit to a 15amp fuseway in the consumer unit, using 2.5mm^2 cable.

Heated towel rail

The Wiring Regulations covering other kinds of heater also apply to a heated towel rail situated in a bathroom. As the towel rail is mounted near the floor, run a flex from it to a flexible-cord outlet, which must in turn be wired to a fused connection unit outside the bathroom. For a towel rail of 1kW or less, fit a 5amp fuse; otherwise, fit a 13amp fuse.

If a heated towel rail is installed in a bedroom, the fused connection unit can be mounted alongside it.

Heat/light unit

Heat/light units, which are sometimes fitted in bathrooms, incorporate a radiant heater and a light fitting in the one appliance. Although they are ceiling-mounted, usually in the position of the ceiling rose, these units must never be connected to lighting circuits.

To install a heat/light unit in this position, turn off the power and, having identified the lighting cables, remove the rose and withdraw the cables into the ceiling void. Fit a junction box to a nearby joist and terminate the lighting cables at that point (3). Don't connect the switch cable, as it won't be needed.

Run a 2.5mm^2 two-core-and-earth spur cable from an unswitched fused connection unit mounted outside the bathroom to a ceiling-mounted 15amp double-pole switch, and from there to the heat/light unit.

Connect up to the fused connection unit (see opposite), then wire the heat/light unit according to the maker's instructions and fit a 13amp fuse in the connection unit.

SEE ALSO	
Details for:	
Bathroom safety	10
Switching off	16
Running cable	23-25
Double-pole ceiling switch	45
Ceiling-rose connections	46

1 Flexible-cord outlet

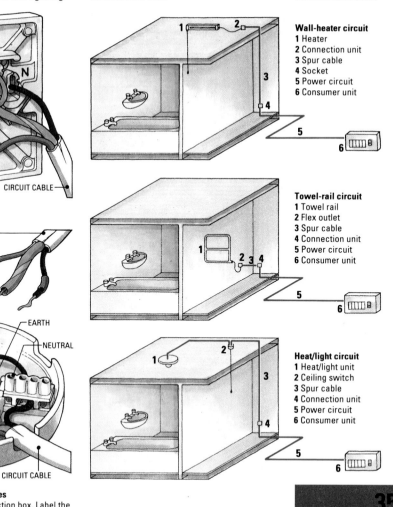

2 Wiring a flexible-cord outlet

DISCONNECTED SWITCH CABLE
CIRCUIT CABLE
EARTH
LIVE
NEUTRAL
CIRCUIT CABLE

3 Terminating the lighting cables
Join the circuit cables in a junction box. Label the disconnected switch wire for future reference.

Wall-heater circuit
1 Heater
2 Connection unit
3 Spur cable
4 Socket
5 Power circuit
6 Consumer unit

Towel-rail circuit
1 Towel rail
2 Flex outlet
3 Spur cable
4 Connection unit
5 Power circuit
6 Consumer unit

Heat/light circuit
1 Heat/light unit
2 Ceiling switch
3 Spur cable
4 Connection unit
5 Power circuit
6 Consumer unit

WIRING
SMALL
APPLIANCES

SEE ALSO

Details for:

Running a spur	31
Fused connection unit	34
Flex outlet	35
30amp double-pole wall switch	39
Double-pole ceiling switch	45
Wiring a shower	45
Connecting to a light circuit	51
Circuit lengths	58

Wall-mounted fan
Run a 1.5mm^2 cable from a fused connection unit to a wall-mounted extractor fan.

Kitchen equipment circuits
1 Connection units
2 Flex outlets
3 Socket outlets

Extractor fan

To install an extractor fan in a kitchen, mount a fused connection unit 150mm (6in) above the worktop and run a cable to the fan or to a flexible-cord outlet next to it. If the fan has no integral switch, use a switched connection unit to control it. Fit a 3 or 5amp fuse as recommended by the manufacturer.

If the fan's speed and direction are controllable, it may have a separate control unit – in which case you need to wire the connection unit to the control unit, following the maker's instructions.

To fit an extractor fan in a bathroom, mount the fused connection unit outside the room and run the cable to the fan or flex outlet via a ceiling-mounted double-pole switch.

Fridges, dishwashers and washing machines

There is no reason why you cannot plug an appliance like a fridge, dishwasher or washing machine into a standard socket outlet – except that in a modern kitchen such appliances are installed under worktops, and sockets mounted behind them are difficult to reach.

It's therefore generally more convenient to mount a switched fused connection unit 150mm (6in) above the worktop, then connect it to the ring circuit and run a spur – using 2.5mm^2 cable – from the connection unit to a socket outlet mounted behind the appliance.

Cooker hood

Either mount a fused connection unit (fitted with a 3amp fuse) close to the cooker hood or mount the connection unit at worktop height and then run a 1mm^2 cable from the unit to a flexible-cord outlet beside the hood.

Instantaneous water heater

You can install an instantaneous water heater above a sink or washbasin in order to provide on-the-spot hot water. Join a 3kW model by heat-resistant flex to a switched fused connection unit mounted out of reach of anyone who is using the water.

If the heater is for use in a bathroom, wire it via a flex outlet to a ceiling pull-switch and then to the connection unit outside the bathroom. The connection unit must be fitted with a 13amp fuse.

Wire a 7kW water heater in the same way as a shower. If it is situated in the kitchen, you can use a double-pole wall switch to control it.

Waste-disposal unit

A waste-disposal unit is housed in the cupboard unit below the sink. Mount a switched fused connection unit 150mm (6in) above a worktop near the sink, but well out of reach of small children and anyone using the sink. From the unit, run a 1mm^2 cable to a flex outlet next to the waste-disposal unit. Clearly label the connection unit 'WASTE DISPOSAL' to avoid accidents. Fit a 13amp fuse.

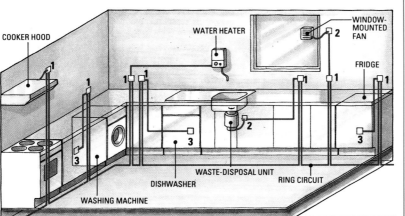

SHAVER SOCKETS

Special shaver socket outlets are the only kind of electrical socket allowed in bathrooms. They contain transformers that isolate the user side of the units from the mains, reducing the risk of an electric shock. This type of socket has to conform to the exacting British Standard BS 3535.

However, there are shaver sockets that do not have isolating transformers and therefore don't conform to BS3535. These are quite safe to install and use in a bedroom, but this type of socket must not be fitted in a bathroom.

You can wire a shaver socket from a junction box on an earthed lighting circuit or from a fused connection unit, fitted with a 3amp fuse, on a ring-circuit spur. If you are installing the shaver socket in a bathroom, then the fused connection unit must be positioned outside the room. Run 1mm^2 two-core-and-earth cable from the connection unit to the shaver socket; then connect the conductors: red to L and black to N **(1)**. Sheath the earth wire with a green-and-yellow sleeve and connect it to E.

Shaver unit for use in a bathroom

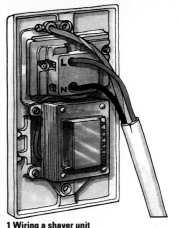

1 Wiring a shaver unit

Powerful appliances such as cookers that have a power load greater than 3000W (3kW) must have their own radial circuits connected directly to the consumer unit, with separate fuses protecting them.

Cookers

Small table cookers and separate ovens that rate no more than 3000W (3kW) can be connected to a ring circuit by a fused connection unit or even by means of a 13amp plug and socket. But most cookers are much more powerful, and must be installed on their own circuits.

The radial circuit
Cookers up to 14kW can be connected on a 30amp radial circuit. Provided that the cooker control unit does not include a 13amp socket outlet, cookers up to 18kW can be connected to a similar circuit. Depending on the length of the relevant circuit, you can use 4mm^2 or 6mm^2 two-core-and-earth cable (see CIRCUITS: MAXIMUM LENGTHS).

A separate radial circuit has to have its own fuseway. You can either use a spare fuseway in your consumer unit or, alternatively, fit an individual switchfuse unit – which performs a similar function to the consumer unit but for a single appliance. Ideally buy a switchfuse unit with a 32amp MCB; failing that, one with a 30amp cartridge fuse.

Cooker control units
The cable from the consumer unit runs to a cooker control unit situated within 2m (6ft 6in) of the cooker. The control unit is basically a double-pole isolating switch, but it may also incorporate a single 13amp switched socket outlet that can be used for appliances such as an electric kettle. Nowadays, when more homes have a number of socket outlets installed at worktop height, the extra one on the cooker control unit is not usually important; and it is in fact safer not to have a control unit with a built-in socket if it is to be situated near the hob – so as to avoid the risk of flex

trailing across one of the hotplates.

Cooker control units can be either surface-mounted or flush-mounted. The control unit must be easily accessible, so don't install it inside a cupboard or under a worktop.

A single control unit can serve both sections of a split-level cooker, with separate cables running to the hob and the oven, provided that the control unit is within 2m (6ft 6in) of both parts. If this isn't possible with your cooker, you will need to install a separate control unit for each part. The connecting cables must be of the same size as the cable used in the radial circuit.

Because a freestanding cooker has to be moved from time to time for cleaning round and behind it, it should be wired with sufficient cable to allow it to be moved well out from the wall. The cable is connected to a terminal outlet box, which is screwed to the wall about 600mm (2ft) above floor level. A fixed cable runs from the outlet box to the cooker control unit.

1 Cooker control unit with socket
2 Basic control unit **3** Terminal outlet box

Cooker circuit
1 Cooker
2 Terminal outlet box
3 Control unit
4 Radial circuit
5 Consumer unit

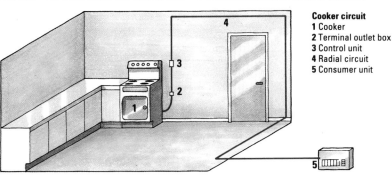

WIRING THE CONTROL UNIT

Having decided on the position for your control unit, if it's to be surface-mounted knock out the cable-entry holes in the mounting box and screw it to the wall. If it's to be flush-mounted, cut a hole in the plaster and brickwork for the metal box.

Running cable
Run and fix the cable, taking the most economical route to the cooker from the switchfuse unit or the consumer unit. Cut a chase in the wall up to the cooker control unit if you are going to bury the cable in the plaster, then cut similar chases for cables running to the separate hob and oven of a split-level cooker or for a single cable running to a terminal outlet box.

Connecting up the control unit
Feed the circuit cable and cooker cable into the control unit, then strip and prepare the conductors for connection. There are two sets of terminals in the control unit: one marked 'Mains' for the circuit conductors, and the other marked 'Load' for the cooker cable. Run the red wires to the L terminals and the black ones to the terminals marked N. Put green-and-yellow sleeves on both earth conductors and connect them to the E terminal (**1**). Screw the faceplate to the mounting box.

RADIAL-CIRCUIT CABLE
TOP
MAINS
LOAD
E
EARTH
CABLE TO OUTLET BOX OR COOKER

1 Wiring the unit
Remove the faceplate to wire some units.

SEE ALSO	
Details for:	
Circuit fuses	19
Stripping cable	22
Running cable	23-25
Flush mounting	29
Switchfuse unit	38
Circuit lengths	58

● **Positioning cooker control units**
Place the control unit to the right or left of the cooker but never directly above it.

CONNECTING THE COOKER

SEE ALSO

Details for:

Testing an installation	9
Switching off	16
Consumer unit	18
Circuit fuses	19
Cables	22
Stripping cable	22
Running cable	23-25

Wiring to the cooker

Connect the cable to the hob and the oven following the manufacturer's instructions exactly.

For a freestanding cooker, run the cable down the wall from the cooker control unit to the terminal outlet box, which has terminals for connecting both of the cables. Strip the wires of the control-unit cable and insert them in the terminals (1), then insert the wires of the cooker cable in the same terminals, matching colour for colour, and secure it with the clamp. Screw the plastic faceplate onto the outlet box.

Wiring the switchfuse unit

If you are wiring to a fuseway in your consumer unit, run the red wire to the terminal on the fuseway, the black one to the neutral block, and – having first sleeved it – the earth wire to the earth block. All other connections will already have been made. Don't forget to switch off the power before starting this work, and remember that even then the cable connecting the meter to the main switch is still live.

Here we will assume that the cooker circuit is to be run from a switchfuse unit. Screw the unit to the wall close to the consumer unit, feed the cooker-circuit cable into it, and prepare the conductors for connection. Fix the red wire to the live terminal on the fuseway or MCB, the black wire to the neutral terminal, and the sleeved earth wire to the earth terminal (2).

Prepare the meter leads, one black and one red, from PVC-sheathed-and -insulated 16mm² single-core cable. (Use 10mm² cable if 16mm² cable is too thick for the switchfuse-unit terminals, but keep the meter leads as short as possible.) Bare about 25mm (1in) of each cable and connect them to their separate terminals on the main isolating switch, red to L and black to N (2). For an earth lead, prepare a similar length of the same size single-core cable sheathed in green-and-yellow PVC and attach it to the earth terminal in the switchfuse unit (2) in readiness for connection to the consumer's earth terminal. Don't make the connection to the Company's earth yourself.

Fit the appropriate fuse, then plug in the fuse carrier. Finally, label the carrier to indicate which circuit is run from the unit and fit the cover.

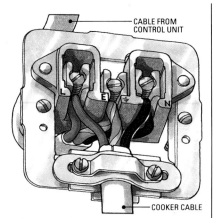

1 Wiring a terminal outlet box

— CABLE FROM CONTROL UNIT

— COOKER CABLE

METER LEADS · — CIRCUIT CABLE
LIVE

NEUTRAL — EARTH LEAD EARTH

2 Wiring a switchfuse unit for the cooker

CONNECTING TO THE MAINS

A new circuit must be tested by a competent electrician and a certificate stating that the wiring complies with the Wiring Regulations must be submitted to the Electricity Company to apply for connecting to the mains. Do not attempt to make this connection (which has to be made via the meter) yourself.

It may not be possible to attach both sets of meter leads – from consumer unit and switchfuse unit – to the meter, and you may have to install a connector block that has enough terminals to accommodate all the conductors. The Electricity Company will do this for a fee (before starting it's advisable to consult the Company about these matters).

Water in a storage cylinder can be heated by an electric immersion heater, providing a central supply of hot water for the whole house. The heating element is rather like a larger version of the one that heats an electric kettle. It is normally sheathed in copper, but more expensive sheathings of incoloy or titanium will increase the life of the element in hard-water areas.

Adjusting the water temperature

A thermostat to control the maximum temperature of the water is set by adjusting a screw inside the plastic cap that covers the terminal box (1).

Types of immersion heater

An immersion heater can be installed from the top of the cylinder or from the side, and top-entry units can have single or double elements. In the single-element top-entry type of heater the element extends down almost to the bottom of the cylinder, so that all of the water is heated whenever the heater is switched on (2).

For economy, one of the elements in the double-element type is a short one for daytime top-up heating, while the other is a full-length element that heats the entire contents of the cylinder, using the cheaper night-rate electricity (3). A double-element heater that has a single thermostat is called a twin-element heater; one with a thermostat for each element is known as a dual-element heater.

Side-entry elements are of identical length. One is positioned near to the bottom of the cylinder, and the other a little above half way up (4).

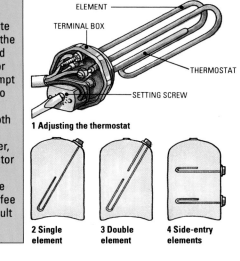

ELEMENT —

TERMINAL BOX

— THERMOSTAT

— SETTING SCREW

1 Adjusting the thermostat

2 Single element **3 Double element** **4 Side-entry elements**

HEATING WATER ON THE NIGHT RATE

If you agree to have a special meter installed, the Electricity Company will supply you with cheap-rate power for seven hours sometime between midnight and 8.00 a.m., the exact period being at the discretion of the Company. This scheme is called Economy 7. Provided you have a cylinder that is large enough to store hot water for a day's requirements, you can benefit by heating all your water during the Economy 7 hours. Even if you heat your water electrically only in summer, the scheme may be worthwhile. For the water to retain its heat all day, you must have an efficient insulating jacket fitted to the cylinder or a cylinder already factory-insulated with a layer of heat-retaining foam.

If your cylinder is already fitted with an immersion heater, you can use the existing wiring by fitting an Economy 7 programmer, a device that will switch your immersion heater on automatically at night and heat up the whole cylinder. Then if you occasionally run out of hot water during the day, you can always adjust the programmer's controls to boost the temperature briefly, using the more expensive daytime rate.

You can make even greater savings if you have two side-entry immersion heaters or a dual-element one. The programmer will switch on the longer element – or the bottom one – at night, but if the water needs heating during the day then the upper element is used.

You can have a similar arrangement without a programmer by wiring two separate circuits for the elements. The upper element is wired to the daytime supply, while the lower one is wired to its own switchfuse unit and operated by the Economy 7 time switch during the hours of the night-time tariff only. A setting of 75°C (167°F) is recommended for the lower element, and 60°C (140°F) for the upper one. If your water is soft or your heater elements are sheathed in titanium or incoloy, you can raise the temperatures to 80°C (175°F) and 65°C (150°F) respectively without reducing the life of the elements.

To ensure you never run short of hot water, leave the upper unit switched on permanently. It will only start heating up if the thermostat detects a temperature of 60°C (140°F) or less, which should happen very rarely if you have a large, properly insulated cylinder.

The circuit

Immersion heaters are mostly rated at 3kW – but although you can wire most 3kW appliances to a ring circuit, an immersion heater is regarded as using 3kW continuously, even though rarely switched on all the time. A continuous 3kW load would seriously reduce a ring circuit's capacity, so immersion heaters must have their own radial circuits.

The circuit needs to be run in 2.5mm² two-core-and-earth cable protected by a 15amp fuse. Each element must have a two-pole isolating switch mounted near the cylinder; the switch should be marked 'WATER HEATER' and have a neon indicator (1). A 2.5mm² heat-resistant flexible cord runs from the switch to the immersion heater.

If the cylinder is situated in a bathroom, the switch must be inaccessible to anyone who is using the washbasin or the bath or shower. If this precludes a normal water-heater switch, use a 20amp ceiling-mounted pull-switch with a mechanical ON/OFF indicator.

Wiring side-entry heaters

For simplicity use two switches, one for each heater and marked accordingly.

Wiring the switches

Fix the mounting boxes to the wall, feed a circuit cable to each, and wire them in the same way. Strip and prepare the wires, then connect them to the 'Mains' terminals – red to L, black to N. Sheath the earth wire in a green-and-yellow sleeve and fix it to the common earth terminal (2). Prepare a heat-resistant flex for each switch. At each, connect the green-and-yellow earth wire to the common earth terminal and the other wires to the 'Load' terminals – brown to L and blue to N (2). Then tighten the flex clamps and screw on the faceplates.

Wiring the heaters

The flex from the upper switch goes to the top heater, and that from the lower switch to the bottom one. At each heater, feed the flex through the hole in the cap and prepare the wires. Connect the brown wire to one terminal on the thermostat (the other terminal on the thermostat is already connected to the wire running to an L terminal of the heating element). Connect the blue wire to the N terminal and the green-and-yellow wire to the E terminal (3), then replace the caps on the terminal boxes.

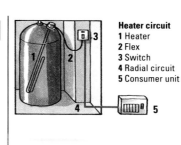

Heater circuit
1 Heater
2 Flex
3 Switch
4 Radial circuit
5 Consumer unit

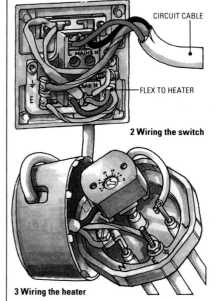

CIRCUIT CABLE

FLEX TO HEATER

2 Wiring the switch

3 Wiring the heater

Running the cable

Run the circuit cables from the cylinder cupboard to the fuse board; then, with the power switched off, connect the cable from the upper heater to a spare fuseway in the consumer unit. Although the consumer unit is switched off, the cable between the main switch and the meter will remain live – so take special care. Wire the other cable to its own switchfuse unit – or to your storage-heater consumer unit, if you have one – ready for connection to the Economy 7 time switch. Make the connections as described for a cooker circuit.

WIRING A DUAL-ELEMENT IMMERSION HEATER

Wire the immersion-heater circuit as described above, but feed the flex from both switches into the cap on the heater. Connect the brown wire from the upper switch to the L2 terminal on one thermostat and the other brown wire to the L1 terminal on the second thermostat (4). Connect the blue wires to their respective neutral terminals (4). Connect both earth wires to E terminal.

Details for:	
Economy 7	6
Switching off	16
Consumer unit	18, 38
Cooker circuit	37-38
Circuit lengths	58

1 A 20amp switch for an immersion heater

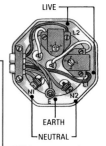

LIVE

L2

N1 — E — N2

EARTH

NEUTRAL

4 Make sure your heater is fitted with two thermostats as shown.

STORAGE HEATERS

SEE ALSO
Details for:
Running a spur 31
Fused connection unit ... 34
Storage heaters 59

The heart of a storage heater is a heat-retaining core, or block, that houses heating elements which are supplied with electricity during the off-peak night-time hours to take advantage of the cheap Economy 7 tariff. The storage core is insulated in such a way that it will give off heat gradually during the day. Heat emission is controlled in various ways.

With the earliest storage heaters it was not possible to control the rate of heat emission, and towards the end of the day emission tended to lessen. This is no longer a problem. Modern heaters have dampers to regulate the flow of air through the core and control the rate of heat loss. Some heaters have dampers that are automatically controlled by circuits that monitor the air temperature in the room.

Research has shown that a cold day is usually preceded by a proportionally cold night – and the more sophisticated storage heaters are designed to make use of this fact by storing just the right amount of heat during the night to meet the needs of the following day.

Fan-assisted storage heaters have a similar heat-retaining core, which is efficiently insulated to reduce heat loss to an absolute minimum. When the fan is switched on, it draws air into the heater to be warmed before flowing out into the room. Apart from a very small amount of radiant heat through the casing, heat emission occurs only

when required, particularly if the fan is controlled thermostatically.

Storage heaters vary in size. Ratings of ones without fans range from 1.2kW to 3.4kW, and fan-assisted models are rated even higher (up to 6kW). A large area requires a heater with a big heat-retaining core able to store enough heat to warm it; and since cheap-rate power is supplied for only a few hours, a large core needs more powerful elements to charge it completely.

When you install storage heaters, you have to assemble them yourself. Follow the manufacturer's instructions exactly, and handle the heating elements and insulation with care. Make sure that slim heaters are fixed securely to the walls – but leave a 75mm (3in) gap all round so that the air can circulate. Use fibre wall plugs for the fixings, as plastic ones may be softened by the heat.

Drying clothes on a storage heater is likely to make a fusible link in the unit melt. Never assemble or dismantle old secondhand storage heaters – they may contain asbestos.

Storage-heater circuits

Unlike other kinds of electrical heating, all the storage heaters in a house are usually switched on at the same time – a procedure that would overload a ring circuit. You therefore have to provide an individual radial circuit for each heater. A separate consumer unit is installed to cope with the off-peak load.

It's wise to choose a consumer unit that is not only large enough to take all

the heater circuits but has spare fuse-ways for possible additional heaters in the future. Make sure there is an extra fuseway to take the immersion-heater circuit, so your water can be heated at the off-peak rate too. A circuit for an ordinary storage heater up to 3.6kW should be wired with 2.5mm^2 two-core-and-earth cable with a 15amp circuit fuse or 16amp MCB.

Outlets for storage heaters

The circuit cable for an ordinary storage heater should terminate at a 20amp double-pole switch with a flex outlet (1) that fits into a standard plastic or metal mounting box. A three-core heat-resistant flex connects the switch to the storage heater.

A fan-assisted heater needs a more complex circuit. The heating elements are supplied from a straightforward radial circuit using 4mm^2 cable, but the fan requires its own circuit for daytime use. Take a spur from a ring circuit to a fused connection unit that has a 3amp fuse, and run a 1.5mm^2 two-core-and-earth cable from the unit for the fan. The heater and fan circuits both terminate at a special dual switch (2) where fan and heater can be isolated simultaneously. Two lengths of heat-resistant flex run from the switch, one to the heater, the other to the fan. A dual switch can be surface-mounted or flush-mounted.

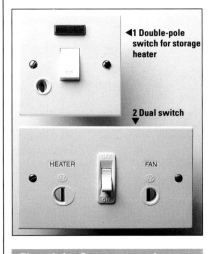

◄1 Double-pole switch for storage heater

2 Dual switch ▼

HEATER   FAN

Electricity Company equipment

Because an Economy 7 storage-heater system uses cheap-rate power, you need a special meter that registers the number of units consumed during the night-time and daytime separately. You also need a time switch to connect the various circuits at the appropriate time.

This equipment is supplied by the Electricity Company, whom you should contact for advice as soon as possible if you plan to have storage heaters. At the same time make sure your present electrical installation is safe, especially the provision for earthing – otherwise the Company may refuse to connect the new circuits.

Storage-heater circuits
1 Off-peak consumer unit
2 Day-time consumer unit
3 Radial circuits to heaters
4 20amp switch
5 Storage heater
6 Fan-assisted storage heater
7 Dual switch
8 Connection unit
9 Ring circuit

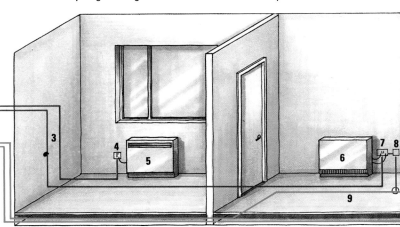

Details for:	
Stripping flex	13
Fuses/MCBs	19
Cables	22
Stripping cable	22
Running cable	23-25
Running a spur	31
Circuit lengths	58

For ordinary storage heaters, mount a 20amp switch close to where you are planning to stand each heater. Run a single length of 2.5mm² two-core-and-earth cable from each switch to the site of the new consumer unit, taking the most economical route.

Feed a cable into the mounting box of each switch, then strip and prepare the wires and connect them up to the 'Mains' terminals: red to L, black to N. Sleeve the earth wire and connect it to the E terminal (1).

Pass the flex from each heater through the outlet hole in the faceplate of its switch. Strip and prepare the wires, then connect them to the 'Load' terminals: brown to L, blue to N, and the green-and-yellow earth wire to E (1). Tighten the cord clamp and fix the switch into its mounting box.

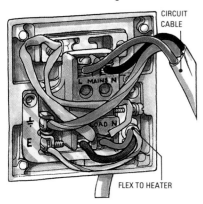

1 Wiring a 20amp switch for a storage heater

Wiring fan-assisted heaters
When you wire a fan-assisted heater, mount a dual switch nearby and from its 'heater' side (2) run a 4mm² two-core-and-earth cable to the consumer unit.

Mount a fused connection unit near the switch and run a short length of 1.5mm² two-core-and-earth cable between the two, connecting to the 'Load' side of the connection unit and the 'Fan' side of the dual switch (2).

Run a spur of 2.5mm² two-core-and-earth cable from the 'Mains' terminals on the connection unit (2) to either a junction box or a socket outlet on the nearest ring circuit.

Feed the fan and heater flex into the outlets in the faceplate of the dual switch and strip and prepare the wires. Connect each flex to its own part of the switch, which is clearly labelled (2).

Tighten the cord clamps and screw the switch to its box.

WIRING THE CONSUMER UNIT

For ordinary storage heaters, fit a 15amp cartridge fuse or 16amp MCB for each heater circuit, and a similar fuse or MCB for an immersion-heater circuit if required. Mount the unit on an exterior-grade plywood board 9mm (⅜in) thick. Even if there's sufficient room, don't mount it on the Electricity Company's meter board

Screw your board to the wall, using plastic or ceramic insulators to space it away, so that damp won't penetrate it. Get the insulators when you buy the consumer unit. Position the board close to the meter to keep the meter leads as short as possible. Screw the consumer unit to the board; run the circuit cables from the heaters into it one at a time; then prepare the wires for connection.

Each circuit is wired in the same way to a separate fuseway: the red wire to the terminal on the fuseway, the black one to the neutral block, and the earth wire to the earth block after sheathing it with a green-and-yellow sleeve.

Use 16mm² single-core cable for the meter leads. They must be insulated and sheathed in red for the live conductor and black for the neutral. Feed the leads into the consumer unit and connect them to their terminals –red to L, black to N – on the main isolating switch.

Next, connect a length of green-and-yellow 16mm² single-core cable to the earth block. Connect the other end to the consumer's earth terminal, and a further length of the same-size cable to the same earth terminal – this will be connected to the Electricity Company's earth by their representative.

Fit MCBs, or clip a fuse into each of the fuse carriers and insert the carriers into their fuseways. Label all of the circuits clearly so that in future you can tell which heater each one supplies.

Fit the cover on the consumer unit and test the circuits. Submit a signed test certificate to the Company, giving them three days' notice, and they will connect the unit to the meter and earth. Don't in any circumstances try to make these connections yourself.

● **Fuses and MCBs for fan-assisted heaters**
You will need to fit a 30amp circuit fuse or a 32amp MCB for each fan-assisted storage heater (see CIRCUITS: MAXIMUM LENGTHS).

Wiring the consumer unit for ordinary storage heaters

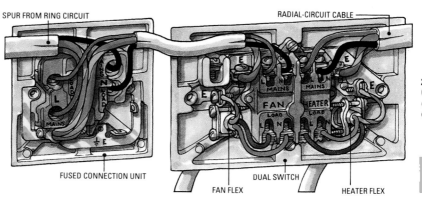

2 **Wiring a dual switch**
Connect a fused connection unit to the dual switch.

DOORBELLS, BUZZERS AND CHIMES

SEE ALSO

Details for:
Consumer unit	18, 38
Running cable	23-25
Running a spur	31
Connecting to a light circuit	51

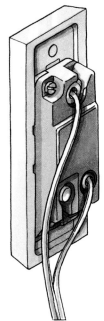

Chimes
A set of chimes has two tubes, each tuned to a different note.

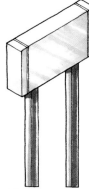

1 Wiring a bell push

Whether you choose a doorbell, a buzzer or a set of chimes, there are no practical differences that affect the way they are installed.

Bells

Most doorbells are of the 'trembler' type. When electricity is supplied to the bell – that is when someone presses the button at the door – it activates an electro-magnet which causes a striker to hit the bell. But as the striker moves to the bell it breaks a contact, cutting off power to the magnet, so the striker swings back, makes contact again and repeats the process, going on for as long as the button is depressed. This type of bell can be operated by battery or, if it is an AC bell, by a mains transformer which may be inside the unit or mounted separately.

Buzzers

A buzzer operates on exactly the same principle as a trembler bell, but in the buzzer the striker hits the magnet itself instead of a bell.

Chimes

A set of ordinary door chimes has two tubes or bars tuned to different notes. Between them is a solenoid, a wound coil that acts like a magnet when it is energized. When the button is pressed, a spring-loaded plunger inside the solenoid is thrown against one tube, sounding a note. When the button is released, the spring throws the plunger against the other tube, sounding the other note before returning to its point of rest. You can also buy chimes with a programmed microprocessor that gives a choice of tunes when operated by the bell push. Most chimes can be run from a battery or a transformer.

Bell pushes

Pressing a bell push completes the circuit that supplies power to the bell. It is in effect a switch that is operated by holding it in the 'on' position. Inside it are two contacts to which the circuit wires are connected. One contact is spring-loaded, touching the other when the button is depressed, to complete the circuit, and then springing back again when the button is released (**1**).

Illuminated bell pushes incorporate a tiny bulb, which enables you to see the bell push in the dark. These have to be operated from a mains transformer – as the power to the bulb, although only a trickle, is on continuously and would soon drain a battery. Luminous types glow at night without a power supply.

Batteries or transformer?

Some bells and chimes house batteries inside the casing, while other types incorporate a built-in transformer that reduces the 240-volt mains electricity to the very low voltages needed for this kind of equipment. For many doorbells or chimes you can use either method. Most of them take either two or four 1½ volt batteries, but some need a 4½ volt battery that is housed separately.

Transformers sold for use with door-bell systems have three low-voltage tappings – 3 volt, 5 volt and 8 volt – to cater for various needs. Usually 3 volt and 5 volt connections are suitable for bells or buzzers, and the 8 volt tapping is adequate for many sets of chimes.

However, some chimes require a higher voltage, and for these you will need a transformer with 4 volt, 8 volt and 12 volt tappings. A bell transformer must be designed in such a way that the full mains voltage cannot cross over to the low-voltage wiring.

Circuit wiring

The battery, bell push and bell are all connected by two-core insulated 'bell wire'. This fine wire is usually surface run, fixed with small staples, but it can be run under floors and in cupboards too. Bell wire is also used to connect a transformer to a bell and bell push.

Connect a BS 3535 Class 2 double-insulated transformer to a junction box or ceiling rose on a lighting circuit with 1mm² two-core-and-earth cable. As no earth is required for a double-insulated transformer, cut and tape back the cable's earth wire at the transformer end. Alternatively, run a spur from a ring circuit in 2.5mm² two-core-and-earth cable to an unswitched fused connection unit fitted with a 3amp fuse; and then run a 1mm² two-core-and-earth cable from the unit to the transformer's 'Mains' terminals. Or you could run 1mm² two-core-and-earth cable directly from a spare 5amp fuseway in your consumer unit.

INSTALLING A SYSTEM

The bell itself can be installed in any convenient position, so long as it is not over a source of heat. The entrance hall is usually best, as a bell there can be heard in most parts of the house. Keep the bell-wire runs as short as possible, especially for a battery-operated bell. With a mains-powered bell you will want to avoid long and costly runs of cable, so place the transformer where it can be wired simply. A cupboard under the stairs is a good place, especially if it is near the consumer unit.

Drill a small hole in the doorframe and pass the bell wire through to the outside. Fix the conductors to the terminals of the bell push, then screw it over the hole.

If the battery is housed in the bell casing, there will be two terminals for attaching the other ends of the wires. Either wire can go to either terminal. If the battery is separate from the bell, run the bell wire from the push to the bell. Separate the conductors, cut one of them and join each cut end to a bell terminal. Run the wire on to the battery and attach it to the terminals (**1**).

If you are wiring to a transformer, proceed as above but connect the bell wire to whichever two of the three terminals combine to provide you with the necessary voltage (**2**). Some bells and chimes require separate lengths of bell wire, one from the bell push and another from the transformer. Fix the wires to terminals in the bell housing, following manufacturer's instructions.

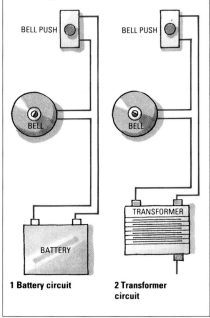

1 Battery circuit   **2 Transformer circuit**

APPLIANCES
TV AERIALS

WIRING
EXTRA AERIAL
SOCKETS
SEE ALSO

Details for:
| Running cable | 23-25 |
| Mounting boxes | 28-29 |

Many people operate only one television set from the aerial mounted on the roof of the house, relying on portable aerials for any additional sets. **You can improve reception by extending the main aerial with additional sockets and, at the same time, provide for viewing a video-cassette recorder from any of your television sets.**

One convenient arrangement is to connect the output socket from your VCR to a double aerial socket, which acts as a 'splitter', diverting the signal to two television sets. Each set will work independently of the other.

If you want to serve even more sets, you will probably have to substitute a multi-output amplifier in place of the splitter in order to boost the signal. An amplifier is wired in a similar way to the splitter socket, but must also be plugged into a 13amp socket.

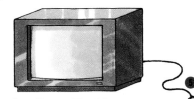
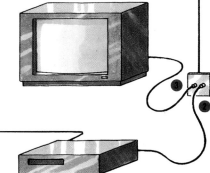
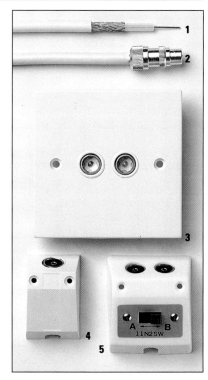

Extending your TV aerial
1 Cable from roof aerial plugs directly into VCR.
2 Output from VCR plugs into double splitter socket.
3 Aerial cable from first TV set plugs into splitter.
4 Coaxial cable runs from the back of the splitter to a single aerial socket.
5 Aerial cable from second TV set plugs into single socket.

CONNECTING COAXIAL PLUGS

Slide the plug's locking ring (1) onto the coaxial cable and strip about 25mm (1in) of the sheathing, taking care not to sever the copper strands beneath. Slide the cable gripper (2) onto the end of the sheathing, then unravel the copper strands and fold them down over the gripper. Cut off excess strands, leaving enough copper to cover the gripper.

Strip all but about 3mm (⅛in) of the polyethylene insulation (3) to reveal the single-core conductor (4). Bend a slight kink in the conductor and insert it in the plug pin (5). Ideally you should secure the conductor with a touch of solder on the tip of the pin, though kinking the conductor usually provides sufficient grip inside the hollow pin. Slide the plug body (6) over the whole assembly and secure it with the locking ring.

1   2   3   4   5   6

Wiring a coaxial plug

Cable and equipment

Aerial sockets are wired with coaxial cable that consists of a single-core solid-copper conductor insulated with polyethylene, which is surrounded by a braided conductor woven from many fine copper strands then sheathed in white, brown or black PVC. Most electrical suppliers stock the required 75ohm cable (1). Coaxial cable is either wired directly into the back of aerial sockets or fitted with special plugs (2) for insertion into the sockets.

Single and double aerial sockets are made with square faceplates (3) for attaching to standard plastic or metal mounting boxes. You can also buy small surface-mounted sockets (4) suitable for screwing to skirting boards.

A double socket can serve to split the incoming signal to two television sets, but if the signal is weak you may find reception is not satisfactory. In that case, either install a signal amplifier or use a switched splitter (5), which allows you to divert the full-strength signal to one set or the other at will.

It is simplest to install only 'female' sockets – those that have holes which accept 'male' coaxial plugs – and fit this type of plug only on all your aerial-extension cables.

1   2   3   4   A 1 1 N 2 SW B   5

Cable, plugs and sockets
1 Coaxial cable 2 Coaxial plug 3 Double-socket faceplate 4 Surface-mounted socket 5 Switched splitter socket

Running coaxial cable

Fit mounting boxes or screw sockets to the skirting in convenient positions for your VCR and television sets, then cut suitable lengths of coaxial cable to run from socket to socket. Although it's quite safe to leave coaxial cable as temporary unfixed 'leads', you can conceal cable runs under floorboards and inside wall cavities – in the same way as you would mains cable. Avoid taking the cable around tight bends.

Wiring the splitter

Prepare a length of coaxial cable to connect the back of the double socket that is to act as the splitter to the back of the single remote socket. Strip about 50mm (2in) of sheathing from the splitter end of the cable and fold back the braided copper strands. Strip about 32mm (1¼in) of insulation from the single-core conductor, then pass the conductor through both terminals (6) and tighten the terminal screws. Fold back the braided copper and trap it along with the cable under the metal clamp (6). Trim off excess copper strands, and then screw the faceplate to the mounting box. The remote socket is wired in a similar way.

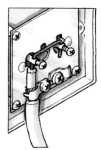

6 Wiring a double socket as a splitter

INSTALLING
A TELEPHONE
EXTENSION

SEE ALSO
Details for:
Running cable   23-25
Mounting boxes   28-29

Although a telephone company such as British Telecom, Mercury Communications Ltd. or Kingston upon Hull Telephone Department must be employed to install the master socket that is connected to the incoming network cable, you are permitted to install extension cables and sockets yourself. All the necessary equipment is available from DIY outlets or from one of the telephone company's own shops.

You can install as many telephone extension sockets as you want – so long as the total 'Ringer Equivalence Number' (REN) in your house or flat does not exceed four. A telephone is normally allocated an REN of one, but it is advisable to check this before you decide which equipment to purchase. Telephones are made with either 'tone' or 'pulse' dialling, and modern phones can be switched from one to the other. However, the type of dialling does not affect the wiring of extension sockets.

Sockets and accessories
1 Single-socket faceplate
2 Surface-mounted socket
3 Socket doubler
4 Converter plug
5 British Telecom Linebox
6 Insertion tool

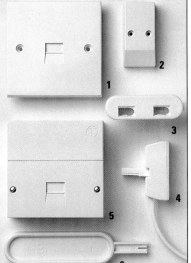

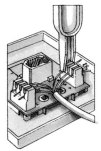

1 Connecting cable to blade terminals
There will be two identical wires per terminal in some sockets.

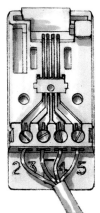

2 Insert wires into screw terminals

Telephone sockets

Single and double sockets designed to accept the small rectangular telephone plugs are made in the form of square faceplates (1) that fit standard electrical metal and plastic mounting boxes. Alternatively, use compact surface-mounted sockets (2). You can run two telephones – or a telephone and an answering machine – from a single socket, without additional wiring, simply by plugging in a 'socket doubler' (3). Run your extension from any master socket by means of a converter plug (4), which normally comes complete with several metres of cable. However, you can wire your extension cable directly into a British Telecom Linebox (5), which has a removable cover to provide customer access without disturbing the company's wiring.

TELEPHONE CABLE

Telephones, including extensions, are wired with special extra-low-voltage cable. This cable usually comprises six colour-coded conductors sheathed in PVC. However, four-core cable is often sold for running domestic telephone extensions, and is perfectly adequate provided you match the colour-coded conductors to any existing wiring (see chart below).

Socket terminals are numbered 1 to 6. Always match the same colour coding to the same number terminal in each socket. If you are using four-core cable, ignore terminals 1 and 6.

Number	Colour coding
Terminal 1	Green with white rings.
Terminal 2	Blue with white rings.
Terminal 3	Orange with white rings.
Terminal 4	White with orange rings.
Terminal 5	White with blue rings.
Terminal 6	White with green rings.

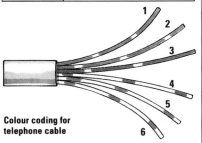

Colour coding for telephone cable

Running the circuit

Fix the extension sockets where most convenient and run a length of cable from the existing master socket to each of the extension sockets. The cable can be pinned to the top of skirting boards or along picture rails and doorframes, using small plastic cable clips.

Alternatively, you can conceal the cable under the floorboards or within walls, provided that you do not follow exactly the same route used for any mains wiring. Both for safety's sake and in order to avoid interference on the line, you should maintain a minimum of 75mm (3in) between telephone cable and mains cables. At each socket, feed a loop of cable into the mounting box ready for connecting to the terminals.

Connecting to the sockets

At each socket, cut the loop of cable and strip the sheathing to expose the colour-coded conductors, then separate the conductors and connect them to the appropriate numbered terminals.

Telephone-socket terminals usually comprise two opposing brass blades that cut into the cable's insulation and make contact with the wire core as the conductor is forced between them with a special insertion tool. Lay the insulated conductor across its terminal, and press it firmly to the base of the terminal (1). Trim the end of the wire.

Other sockets are made with screw terminals, similar to those found in 13amp plugs. Strip about 6mm (¼in) of insulation from the end of each of the conductors, then insert the wire into the terminal and tighten the screw (2).

Sometimes, plastic cable ties are provided to secure the cable inside the socket in order to prevent strain on the actual connections.

Connecting to the master socket

Plugging a converter plug into the master socket connects all your extensions to the telephone company network. To connect cable to a British Telecom Linebox, remove the front cover (3) and use the insertion tool to introduce the conductors into the bladed terminals, as described left.

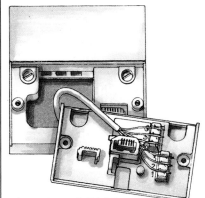

3 Connecting to a British Telecom Linebox

SEE ALSO	
Details for:	
Bonding to earth	10
Consumer unit	18
Circuit fuses	19
Cables	22
Running cable	23-25
Switchfuse unit	38
Fixing to ceiling	47
Circuit lengths	58

WIRING A SHOWER UNIT

An electrically heated shower unit is plumbed into the mains water supply. The flow of water operates a switch to energize an element that heats the water on its way to the shower spray-head. Because there is so little time to heat the flowing water, instantaneous showers use a heavy load, from 6 to 9.6kW. Consequently, an electrically heated shower unit has to have a separate radial circuit, which must be protected by a 30 milliamp RCD.

The circuit cable needs to be 10mm² two-core-and-earth, protected by a 40amp MCB or a 45amp fuse in a spare fuseway at the consumer unit or in a separate 45amp switchfuse unit. The cable runs directly to the shower unit, where it must be wired according to the manufacturer's instructions.

The shower unit itself has its own on/off switch, but there must also be a separate isolating switch in the circuit. This must not be accessible to anyone using the shower, so install a ceiling-mounted 45amp double-pole pull-switch that has a contact gap of at least 3mm, preferably with a neon 'on' indicator. Fix the backplate of the switch to the ceiling and, having sheathed the earth wires with a green-and-yellow sleeve, connect them to the E terminal on the switch. Connect the conductors from the consumer unit to the switch's 'Mains' terminal, and those of the cable to the shower to the 'Load' terminals (1).

The shower unit and all metal pipes and fittings must be bonded to earth.

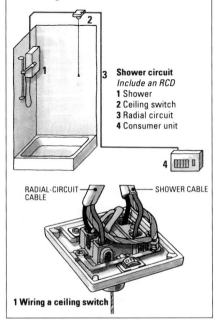

Shower circuit
Include an RCD
1 Shower
2 Ceiling switch
3 Radial circuit
4 Consumer unit

RADIAL-CIRCUIT
CABLE
SHOWER CABLE

1 Wiring a ceiling switch

Every lighting system needs a feed cable to supply power to all the lighting points, and a switch that can interrupt the supply to each point. There are two ways of meeting these requirements in your home: the junction-box system and the loop-in system. Your house may be wired with either one, though it is quite likely that there will be a combination of the two systems.

The junction-box system
With a junction-box system, a two-core-and-earth feed cable runs from a fuse-way in the consumer unit to a series of junction boxes, one for each lighting point. From the junction box, a separate cable runs to the light itself and another runs to its switch.

The loop-in system
In the loop-in system the ceiling rose takes the place of the junction box. The cable from the consumer unit runs into each rose and out again, then on to the next. The switch cable and the flex to the bulb are connected at the rose.

Combined system
The loop-in system is now more widely used since it entails fewer connections, as well as saving on the cost of junction boxes. However, lights located at some distance from a loop-in circuit are often run from a junction box on the circuit in order to save cable, and lights added after the circuit has been installed are often wired from junction boxes.

The circuit
Both the junction-box and the loop-in systems are, in effect, multi-outlet radial circuits. The cable runs from the consumer unit, looping in and out of the ceiling roses or junction boxes and terminating at the last one. Unlike the cable of a ring circuit, it doesn't return to the consumer unit.

Lighting circuits require 1mm² or 1.5mm² PVC-insulated-and-sheathed two-core-and-earth cable, and each circuit is protected by a 5amp circuit fuse or 6amp MCB. A maximum of twelve 100W bulbs or their equivalent can therefore use the circuit.

In the average two-storey house the usual practice is to have two separate lighting circuits – one for the ground floor and another for upstairs.

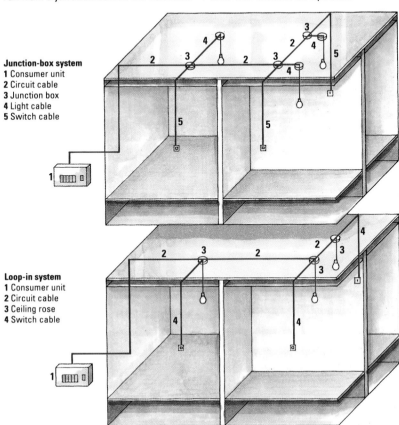

Junction-box system
1 Consumer unit
2 Circuit cable
3 Junction box
4 Light cable
5 Switch cable

Loop-in system
1 Consumer unit
2 Circuit cable
3 Ceiling rose
4 Switch cable

IDENTIFYING THE CONNECTIONS

SEE ALSO
Details for:
Lighting circuits   45

Loop-in system

A modern loop-in ceiling rose has three terminal blocks, which are arranged in a row. The live (red) conductors from the two cut ends of the circuit-feed cable run to the live central block, and the neutral (black) conductors run to the neutral block on one side. The earth conductors (green-and-yellow) run to a common earth terminal (**1**).

The live (red) wire from the switch cable is connected to the remaining terminal in the live central block. The electricity runs through this wire to the switch, then back to the ceiling rose via the black conductor – the 'switch-return wire' – which is connected to the third terminal block in the ceiling rose (the 'switch-wire block'). When the light is 'on', the switch-return wire is live – it

is therefore important to identify it by wrapping a piece of red tape round it to distinguish it from the other black wires, which are neutral. The earth conductor in the switch cable goes to the common earth terminal (**1**).

The brown (live) conductor from the flex of the pendant light connects to the remaining terminal in the switch block, while the blue conductor runs to the neutral block. If three-core flex is used, the green-and-yellow earth conductor runs to the common earth terminal (**1**).

If the circuit-feed cable terminates at the last ceiling rose on the circuit, then only one set of cable conductors is connected (**2**). The switch cable and the light flex are connected in the same way as those in a normal loop-in rose.

Junction-box system

The junction boxes on a lighting circuit normally have four unmarked terminals, for live, neutral, earth and switch connections. The live, neutral and earth conductors from the circuit-feed cable go to their respective terminals (**3**).

The live (red) conductor from the cable that runs to the ceiling rose has to be connected to the switch terminal; the black wire to the neutral terminal; and the green-and-yellow earth wire to the earth terminal (**3**).

The red wire from the switch cable is connected to the live terminal; the earth conductor to the earth terminal; and the black 'return' wire (see above) from the switch goes to the switch terminal

(**3**). This last conductor must be clearly identified by having a piece of red tape wrapped round it.

At the ceiling rose the live cable conductor is connected to one of the outer terminal blocks, and the neutral conductor to the other one. The central block is left empty. The earth conductor goes to the earth terminal (**4**).

The flex conductors are wired up to match those from the cable. The brown wire is connected to the same terminal block as the red conductor, and the blue wire goes to the block holding the black conductor. If the flex has a green-and-yellow earth wire, it is connected to the common earth terminal (**4**).

Checking an old light circuit

Having first switched off the power at the consumer unit, remove the circuit fuse and examine the ceiling roses and light switches for signs of deterioration.

In the majority of houses and flats built before World War II the wiring of the lighting circuits was carried out in rubber-insulated-and-sheathed cable. If the rubber sheathing has become dry and crumbly, it is no longer safe and the circuit must be rewired. If you detect any signs that the circuitry is out of date or merely suspect it may be dangerous, consult a professional electrician.

An old installation may have loop-in or junction-box lighting circuits, though the junction-box system is more likely. It may also lack earth conductors, which is another good reason for renewing it.

Old fabric-covered flex should be replaced

CONNECTIONS FOR LOOP-IN AND JUNCTION-BOX SYSTEMS

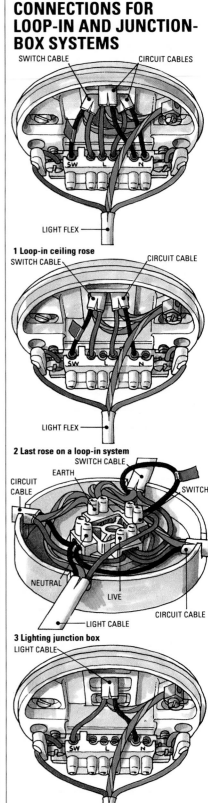

1 Loop-in ceiling rose

2 Last rose on a loop-in system

3 Lighting junction box

4 Ceiling rose on a junction-box system

REPLACING A CEILING ROSE

Turn off the power at the consumer unit and remove the circuit fuse. Switching off at the wall is not enough.

Unscrew the cover of the rose and examine the connections, so that you can wire the new ones to operate in the same way. If it is a loop-in rose, identify the switch-return wire with red tape if it isn't already marked. If there's only one red and one black conductor, then the rose is on a junction-box system and will therefore have no switch cable.

In an old rose you may have to identify all the wires. If there are wires running into three terminal blocks, look first for the one with all red wires and no flex wires. That is the live block, containing live circuit-feed wires and a live switch wire. The neutral terminal block contains the black neutral circuit-feed wires and the blue flex wire. The third block will contain the brown flex wire plus a black conductor – the switch-return wire – which should be marked with red tape and may even be sheathed in red PVC.

All earth conductors will run to one terminal on the backplate. However, an old system may have no earth wires – in which case reconnect the other wires temporarily and get expert advice on rewiring the circuit.

Fixing the new rose
Disconnect the wires from the terminals and separate any that are twisted together, but identify them with tapes.

Unscrew the old backplate from the ceiling. Knock out the entry hole in the new backplate and thread the cables through it, then fix the backplate to the ceiling, using the old screws and fixing points if possible.

If the old fixings are not secure, nail a piece of wood between the joists above the ceiling (see right) and drill a hole through it from below for cable access. Screw the new rose backplate to the wood through the ceiling.

Make sure that the ends of all the conductors are clean and sound, then rewire the ceiling rose.

Slip the new cover over the pendant flex and connect the flex wires to the terminals in the rose, looping the wires over the rose's support hooks to take the weight off the terminals. Screw the cover onto the backplate, then switch on the power and test the light.

There is now a vast range of lighting fittings that can be used in the home, and though they may differ greatly in their appearance they can be grouped roughly into seven basic categories according to their functions.

Types of light fitting

Pendant lights
The pendant light is probably the most common light fitting. It comprises a lamp-holder with bulb, usually with some kind of shade, suspended from a ceiling rose by a length of flex. The flex is connected to the power supply through terminals inside the ceiling rose (see opposite).

Most decorative pendant-light fittings are designed to take several bulbs, and are consequently heavier than standard pendant lights. Because of its weight, this type of fitting is attached to the ceiling by a rigid tube. The flex that conducts the power to the bulbs passes through the tube to the lighting circuit.

Close-mounted ceiling lights
A close-mounted light fitting is screwed directly to the ceiling, without a ceiling rose, by means of a backplate housing the lampholder or holders. The fitting is usually enclosed by some kind of rigid light-diffuser, which is also attached to the backplate.

Recessed ceiling lights
With this type of light fitting, the lamp housing itself is recessed into the ceiling void, and the diffuser lies flush with, or projects only slightly below, the ceiling. Lights of this type are ideal for rooms with low ceilings; they are often referred to as downlighters.

Track lights
Several individual light fittings can be attached to a metal track which is

screwed to the ceiling or wall. Because a contact runs the length of the track, lights can be fitted anywhere along it.

Fluorescent light fittings
A fluorescent light fitting uses a glass tube containing mercury vapour. The voltage makes electrons flow between electrodes at the ends of the tube and bombard an internal coating – which fluoresces, producing light.

Different types of coating make the light appear 'warmer' or 'cooler'. Choose either 'warm white' or 'daylight' for domestic purposes.

The light fitting, which includes a starter mechanism, is usually mounted directly on the ceiling – though, as they produce very little heat, fluorescent lights are also frequently fitted to the underside of cupboards above kitchen work surfaces.

Compact fluorescent lamps can be used in place of conventional bulbs and last up to eight times longer. The tube is folded to make a very small unit. They either have the control circuits built-in or are supplied with plug-in holders containing these controls. Make sure the light fitting can support the weight of a compact fluorescent lamp.

Wall lights
A light fitting adapted for screwing to a wall instead of a ceiling can be supplied from the lighting circuit in the ceiling void or from a spur off a ring circuit. Various kinds of close-mounted fittings or adjustable spotlights are the most popular wall lights.

SEE ALSO

Details for:	
Lampholders	15
Switching off	16
Close-mounted light	48
Track light	48
Fluorescent light	49
Wall lights	53

Batten holders
A batten holder is a basic fitting with a lamp-holder mounted on a plate that fixes directly to the wall or ceiling. Straight, angled and swivel versions are available. Batten holders are for use in areas such as lofts or cellars where appearance is not important.

Fixing a platform
Skew-nail a board between the joists to support a ceiling rose.

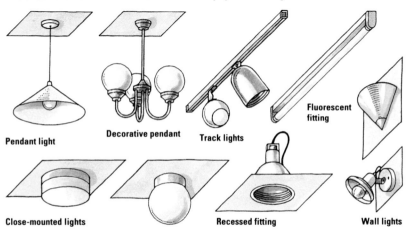

Pendant light

Decorative pendant

Track lights

Fluorescent fitting

Close-mounted lights

Recessed fitting

Wall lights

FITTING A CLOSE-MOUNTED LIGHT

SEE ALSO

Details for:	
Switching off	16
Loop-in system	45, 46
Junction box	46
Close-mounted lights	47
Fixing to ceiling	47
Recessed lights	47
Track lights	47

1 BESA box
Use a BESA box, also known as a conduit box, to house the connections when a light fitting is supplied without a backplate. A metal box must be earthed.

Some close-mounted light fittings have a backplate that screws directly to the ceiling in place of a ceiling rose. To fit one, first switch off the power for the circuit at the consumer unit and take out the fuse, then remove the ceiling rose and fix the backplate to the ceiling.

If only one cable feeds the light, attach its conductors to the terminals of the lampholder and connect the earth wire to the terminal on the backplate.

As more heat will be generated in an enclosed fitting, slip heat-resistant sleeving over the conductors before attaching them to their terminals.

If the original ceiling rose was wired into a loop-in system, then you will find that a close-mounted light fitting won't accommodate all the cables. In which case, withdraw them into the ceiling void and wire them into a junction box screwed to a length of 100 x 25mm (4 x 1in) timber nailed between the joists; then run a short length of heat-resistant cable from the junction box to the new light fitting.

FITTING A PLASTIC BESA BOX

Fix a wooden platform between the ceiling joists to support the junction box and the BESA box.

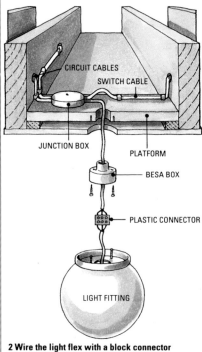

2 Wire the light flex with a block connector

Sometimes close-mounted lights are supplied without backplates.

Wiring Regulations recommend that all unsheathed wires and terminals must be enclosed in a non-combustible housing – so if you want to use a fitting without a backplate you must find a means of complying. The best way is to fit a BESA box (1), a plastic or metal box that is fixed into the ceiling void so as to lie flush with the ceiling.

Screw-fixing lugs on the box should line up with the fixing holes in the light fitting's cover plate, but check that they do so before buying the box. You will also need two machine screws of the right thread for attaching the light to the BESA box.

Check that there is no joist directly above where you wish to fit the light. If there is one, move the light to one side until it fits between two joists. Hold the box against the ceiling, trace round it, and carefully cut the traced shape out of the ceiling with a padsaw.

Cut a fixing board from timber 25mm (1in) thick to fit between the joists, and place it directly over the hole in the ceiling while an assistant marks out the position of the hole on the board from below. Then drill a cable-feed hole centrally through the marked-out shape of the ceiling aperture on the board. This hole must also be able to take any boss on the back of the BESA box. Position the box and screw it securely to the board.

Have your assistant press some kind of flat panel against the ceiling and over the aperture. Fit the BESA box into the aperture from above so that it rests on the panel; mark the level of the fixing board on both joists; and then screw a batten to each joist to support the board at that level.

Fix the board to the battens and feed the cable through the hole in the centre of the BESA box. The light fitting itself will probably have a plastic connector for attaching the cable conductors (2), and this may have three terminals – or, alternatively, a separate terminal for the earth conductor may be attached to the cover plate.

When the conductors are secured, fix the cover plate to the BESA box with the machine screws.

If the original ceiling rose was fed by more than one cable, connect them to a junction box in the ceiling void as described above left.

FITTING A DOWNLIGHTER

Decide where you want the light, check from above that it falls between joists, and then use the cardboard template supplied with all downlighters to mark the outline of the circular aperture in the ceiling. Drill a series of 12mm (½in) holes just inside the perimeter of the marked circle to remove most of the waste, then cut it out with a padsaw.

Bring a single lighting-circuit cable from a junction box through the opening and attach the cable to the downlighter, following the maker's instructions. You may have to fit another junction box into the void in order to connect the circuit cable to the heat-resistant flex attached to the light fitting.

Fit the downlighter into the opening and secure it there by adjusting the clamps that bear on the upper, hidden surface of the ceiling.

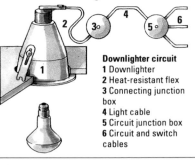

Downlighter circuit
1 Downlighter
2 Heat-resistant flex
3 Connecting junction box
4 Light cable
5 Circuit junction box
6 Circuit and switch cables

FITTING TRACK LIGHTING

Ceiling fixings are supplied with all track-lighting systems. Mount the track so that the terminal-block housing at one end is situated close to where the old ceiling rose was fitted. Pass the circuit cable into the fitting and wire it to the cable-connector provided.

If the circuit is a loop-in system, mount a junction box in the ceiling void to connect the cables.

Make sure that the number of lights you intend to use on the track will not overload the lighting circuit – which can supply a maximum of twelve 100W lamps or their equivalent.

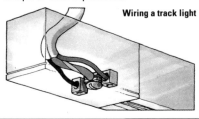

Wiring a track light

SEE ALSO	
Details for:	
Switching off	16
Running cable	23-25
Mounting boxes	28-29
Fused connection unit	34
Junction box	46
Fixing to ceiling	47
Fluorescent lights	47
Wiring switches	50, 52

Fluorescent lights

Fluorescent light fittings are supplied with terminal blocks for connection to the mains supply.

Remove the ceiling rose and then screw the new light fitting to the ceiling, positioned so that the circuit cable can be fed into it conveniently. The terminal block will take only three conductors, so the fitting must be connected to a junction-box system, or a junction box must be installed in the ceiling void to accommodate loop-in wiring as for a close-mounted light (see opposite).

Fluorescent lights normally need earth connections, so they cannot be used on old systems that have no earth conductors.

You can mount a fluorescent unit by screwing directly into ceiling joists or into boards nailed between joists to provide secure fixings.

Wiring a fluorescent light fitting
A simple plastic block connector for the circuit cable is fitted inside a fluorescent light fitting.

FLUORESCENT LIGHTS UNDER CUPBOARDS

You can fit fluorescent lighting to the underside of wall-mounted kitchen cupboards to illuminate the work surfaces below, the power being supplied from a switched fused connection unit fitted with a 3amp cartridge fuse.

You can install a second fluorescent light fitting and supply its power by wiring it into the terminal block of the first one.

The type of switch most commonly used for controlling lighting is the plateswitch. This incorporates a switch mechanism mounted behind a square faceplate with either one, two or three rockers. Although that is generally adequate for domestic purposes, double faceplates that have as many as four or six rockers are also available.

A one-way switch simply turns a light on and off, but two-way switches are wired in pairs so that the light can be controlled from two places – typically, at the head and foot of a staircase. There is also an intermediate switch that allows a light to be controlled from three places.

Any switch can be flush-mounted in a metal box that is buried in the wall, or surface-mounted in a plastic box. Boxes 16 and 25mm (⅝ and 1in) deep are available to accommodate switches of different depths.

A narrow architrave switch can be used where there is not enough room for a standard switch. There are double versions that have two rockers, one above the other.

A dimmer switch is a device that not only turns the light on and off but also controls the intensity of illumination. In some versions a single knob serves as both switch and dimmer. Others have a separate knob for switching, so that the light level does not have to be adjusted every time the light is switched on.

A conventional switch cannot be mounted within reach of a washbasin, bath or shower unit. To comply with the Wiring Regulations, ceiling-mounted double-pole switches with pull-cords are therefore used in bathrooms.

Fixing switches and running cable

Lighting cable is either run underneath floorboards or within the hollow of cavity walls, or is buried in wall plaster. The mounting boxes and switches are fixed to various walls by exactly the same methods as used for sockets.

Light switches must be installed in relatively accessible positions, which normally means at about adult shoulder height for a wall switch and just inside the door of a room.

TYPES OF SWITCHES

Most light switches are made from white plastic, but you can buy more-interesting finishes to compliment your decorative scheme. Bright primary-coloured switches can look striking in a modern house, while brass antique-reproduction switches are attractive in a traditional interior.

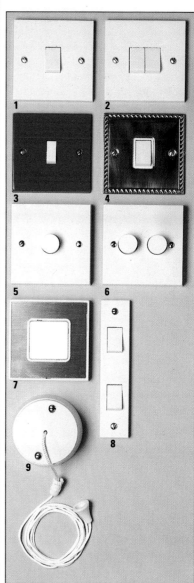

Selection of light switches
1 One-gang rocker switch
2 Two-gang rocker switch
3 Primary-coloured rocker switch
4 Reproduction antique switch
5 One-gang dimmer switch
6 Two-gang dimmer switch
7 Touch dimmer switch
8 Two-gang architrave switch
9 Ceiling switch

REPLACING

SWITCHES

SEE ALSO

Details for:

Switching off	16
Cables	22
Flush mounting	29
Switches	49
Two/three-way lighting	52

Replacing a damaged switch is a matter of connecting the existing wiring to the terminals of the new switch so that it is connected in exactly the same way as it was in the old one.

Always turn off the power and remove the fuse before you take off the faceplate to inspect the wiring.

In the case of a surface-mounted switch, make sure that a new faceplate will fit the existing box – otherwise you will have to replace both parts of the switch.

If you are able to use the old box, use the old machine screws when you attach the new faceplate. You can then be certain of having screws that will match the old threads.

If you want to replace a surface-mounted switch with a flush-mounted one, remove the old switch, then hold the metal box over the position of the original switch and trace round it. Cut away the plaster to the depth of the box and screw it to the brickwork. Take great care not to damage the existing wiring while you are working.

Replacing a one-way switch

If you look at a one-way switch, you will find that it is serviced by a two-core-and-earth cable. The earth conductor, if there is one, will be connected to an earth terminal on the mounting box; and the red and black conductors will be connected to the switch itself.

A true one-way switch has only two terminals, one situated above the other, and the red or black conductors can be connected to either terminal (**1**). The back of the faceplate is marked 'top' to ensure that you mount the switch the right way up, so the rocker is depressed when the light is on. The switch would work just as well upside down – but the 'up for off' convention is a useful one, as it tells you whether the switch is on or off even when the bulb has failed.

Occasionally you may come across a light switch that is fed by a two-core-and-earth cable and operates as a one-way switch, yet has three terminals (**2**). This is a two-way switch that has been wired up for one-way function, something that's fairly common and perfectly safe. If the switch is mounted the right way up, then the red and black wires should be connected to the 'Common' and 'L2' terminals (**2**).

Replacing a two-way switch

A two-way switch will have at least one conductor in each of its three terminals. Without going into the complexities of two-way wiring at this stage, the most straightforward method of replacing a damaged two-way switch is to make a written note of which conductors run to which terminals before disconnecting the various wires.

Another way is to detach the wires from their terminals one at a time, then connect each one to the corresponding terminal on the new two-way switch before dealing with the next conductor.

Two-gang switches

A two-gang switch is the name for two individual switches mounted on a single faceplate. Each of the switches may be wired differently. One may be working as a one-way switch, and the other as a two-way (**3**). To transfer the wires from an old switch to the terminals of a new one, work on one switch at a time and use one of the methods for replacing a two-way switch described above.

Replacing a rocker switch with a dimmer switch

Examine the present switch in order to determine the type of wiring that feeds it, then purchase a dimmer switch that will accommodate the existing wiring. The manufacturers of dimmer switches provide instructions with them, but the connections are basically the same as for ordinary rocker switches (**4**).

Don't attempt to use a dimmer switch to control a fluorescent light.

HOW SWITCHES ARE WIRED

It is very easy to replace a damaged switch or swap one for a switch of a different nature. The illustrations below show four common methods of wiring switches. If one of your switches appears to be wired differently, it is probably part of a two-way or three-way lighting system. Replace the switches as described left.

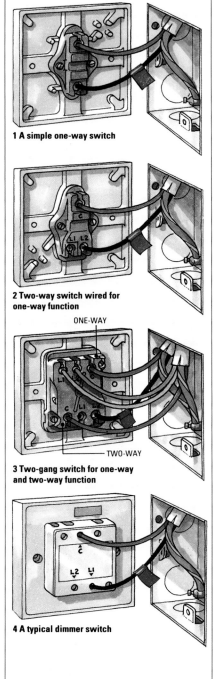

1 A simple one-way switch

2 Two-way switch wired for one-way function

3 Two-gang switch for one-way and two-way function

4 A typical dimmer switch

When you want to move a switch or install one where none existed before, you will have to modify the circuit cables or run a new spur cable from the existing lighting circuit to take the power to where it is needed.

1 Link the switch cable with a junction-box

ADDING NEW SWITCHES AND CIRCUITS

SEE ALSO	
Details for:	
Switching off	16
Cutting a chase	23
Running a cable	23–25
Connecting to junction box	31
Lighting circuits	45
Wiring a rose (last on loop-in)	46
Nail-fixed wood	47
Wiring one-way as two-way	50
Wiring one-way switch	50
Circuit lengths	58

Replacing a wall switch with a ceiling switch

Light switches must be out of reach of anyone using a bath or shower. If your bathroom has a wall switch that breaks this rule, replace it with a ceiling switch that is operated by a pull-cord.

Turn the power off at the consumer unit and remove the old switch. If the cable running up the wall is surface-mounted or in a plastic conduit, you can pull it up into the ceiling void. It should be long enough to reach the point where the new switch is to be located.

If the switch cable is buried in the wall, trace it in the ceiling void and cut it. Then wire the part that runs to the light into a three-terminal junction box fixed to a joist or to a piece of wood nailed between two joists. Connect the conductors to separate terminals **(1)**,

and from those terminals run matching 1mm^2 two-core-and-earth cable to the site of the ceiling switch.

Bore a hole in the ceiling to pass the cable through to the switch. Screw the switch to the joist if the hole is close enough; otherwise fix a support board between joists.

Knock out the entry hole in the backplate of the switch and pass the cable through it, then screw the plate to the ceiling. Strip and prepare the ends of the conductors, connecting the earth to the terminal on the backplate. Connect the red and black conductors to the terminals on the switch – either wire to either terminal **(2)**. Finally, attach the switch to the backplate and make good any damage done to the plasterwork.

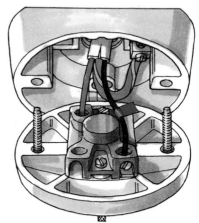

2 Wiring a ceiling switch

Adding a new switch and light

Switch the power off at the consumer unit and inspect your lighting circuit to check whether it is earthed. If there's no earth wire, get expert advice before installing new light fittings.

Decide where you want the light and bore a hole through the ceiling for the cable. Screw a ceiling rose to a nearby joist, or nail a board between two joists to provide a strong fixing for the rose.

Bore another hole in the ceiling right above the site of the new switch and as close to the wall as possible. Push twists of paper through both holes, so you can find them easily from above.

Screw the switch mounting box to the wall and cut a chase in the plaster for the cable up to the appropriate hole already bored in the ceiling.

Your new light fitting can either be supplied from a nearby junction box or ceiling rose that's already on the lighting circuit or, if it is more convenient that way, from a new junction box wired into the lighting-circuit cable.

From whichever of these sources you choose, run a length of 1mm^2 two-core-and-earth cable to the position of the new light – but do not connect the circuit until the whole of the installation is complete. Push the end of the cable through the hole in the ceiling and identify it with tape **(1)**. Write 'Mains' on the tape to be absolutely sure.

The next step is to run a similar cable

from the switch to the same lighting point. Strip and prepare the cable at the switch – connecting the earth wire to the terminal on the mounting box – and connect the red and black conductors, either wire to either terminal if it is a one-way switch. If you are able to obtain only a two-way switch, connect the wires to its 'Common' and 'L2' terminals (see opposite). Now screw the switch to the mounting box.

Knock out the cable-entry hole in the ceiling rose, feed both cables through it, and screw the rose to the ceiling.

Take the cable marked 'Mains' and connect its red conductor to the live central block and its black one to the neutral block. Slip a green-and-yellow sleeve over the earth wire and connect it to the earth terminal.

Connect the red conductor of the switch cable to the live block, and the black wire to the switch-wire block: mark the black wire with red tape. Connect the switch earth wire to the common earth terminal. Screw the cover on the rose.

Make sure the power is turned off, and then connect the new light circuit to the old one at the rose or junction box. The new conductors will have to share terminals that have already been connected: red to live, black to neutral, and earth to earth **(2)**. Finally, test and switch on the new circuit.

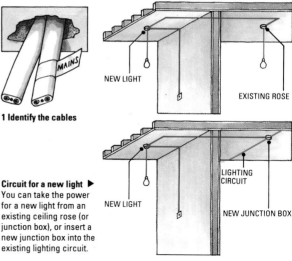

1 Identify the cables

Circuit for a new light ▶
You can take the power for a new light from an existing ceiling rose (or junction box), or insert a new junction box into the existing lighting circuit.

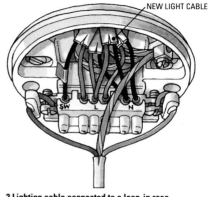

2 Lighting cable connected to a loop-in rose

ADDING TWO- OR THREE-WAY LIGHTING

SEE ALSO

Details for:
Connecting to junction box	31
Lighting circuits	45
Adding new switch and light	51
Connecting to loop-in rose	51
Circuit lengths	58

Adding a two-way light

There are several situations in which a light should be controllable from two points. A hall light is best switched from both ends of the passageway, and a landing light must be controlled from the top and bottom of the stairs.

Installing a new two-way light is very similar to installing a one-way light, the only real difference being in the wiring of the switches.

First mount the ceiling rose and both two-way switches, then run 1mm^2 two-core-and-earth cable from the power source to the light and from the light to the nearest switch. Don't connect the new installation to the circuit till all the wiring has been completed.

Run a 1mm^2 three-core-and-earth cable from the first to the second switch. Then strip the conductors and prepare them for connecting to the switches, slipping insulating sleeves over the bare ends of the earth wires.

At the first switch you will have two cables to connect: the switch cable from the light and the one linking the switches. The switch cable has three conductors (red, black and green-and-yellow); the linking cable has four (red, yellow, blue and green-and-yellow). Take the two green-and-yellow wires, twist their bare ends together and connect them to the earth terminal on the mounting box (1).

Connect the red wire from the linking cable to the 'Common' terminal on the switch. Twist together the ends of the yellow wire and either the red or black switch-cable wire, and connect them to the 'L1' terminal. Twist together the ends of the blue wire and the remaining switch-cable wire, and connect them to the 'L2' terminal (1). Screw the switch's faceplate to the mounting box.

At the second switch, connect the linking cable's green-and-yellow wire to the earth terminal; its red wire to the 'Common' terminal; its yellow wire to 'L1'; and its blue wire to 'L2' (1). Screw the switch's faceplate to the box.

Make sure the power is switched off, and then connect the installation to the lighting circuit at either a ceiling rose or a junction box. Test the new installation.

Three-way lighting

You can control a light from three places by adding an intermediate switch to the circuit described above.

This intermediate switch interrupts the three-core-and-earth cable linking the other two. It has two 'L1' terminals and two 'L2' ones.

At its mounting box you will have two identical sets of wires – red, yellow, blue and green-and-yellow. Connect the green-and-yellow wires to the earth terminal of the box (2) and join the two red wires – which play no part in the intermediate switching – with a plastic block connector (2). Ease the block to one side, in order to clear the switch when you fit it.

Connect the blue and yellow wires of either cable to the 'L1' terminals on the new switch and those of the other cable to the 'L2' terminals (2). Screw the faceplate to the mounting box.

Two-way-lighting circuit (right)
1 Consumer unit
2 Light fitting
3 Lighting-circuit cable
4 Switch cable
5 Switch
6 Linking cable
7 Junction box

Three-way-lighting circuit (far right)
1 Consumer unit
2 Light fitting
3 Lighting circuit
4 Switch cable
5 Switch
6 Intermediate switch
7 Linking cable
8 Junction box

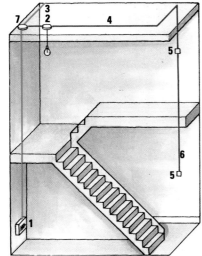

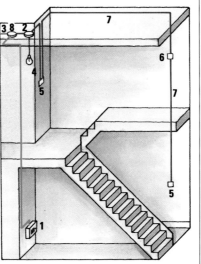

WIRING TWO-WAY AND THREE-WAY SWITCHES

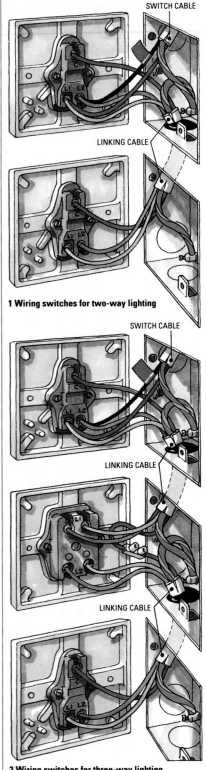

SWITCH CABLE

LINKING CABLE

1 Wiring switches for two-way lighting

SWITCH CABLE

LINKING CABLE

LINKING CABLE

2 Wiring switches for three-way lighting

ADDING
WALL LIGHTS

SEE ALSO	
Details for:	
Switching off	16
Running cable	23-25
Flush mounting	29
Running a spur	31
Fused connection unit	34
Lighting circuits	45
Junction-box connection	46
BESA box	48
Double-gang switch	50
One-way switch	50
Circuit lengths	58

Many wall lights are supplied without integral backplates to enclose the wires and connections. In order to comply with the Wiring Regulations such a fitting must be attached to a non-combustible mounting such as a BESA box – a round plastic or metal box that's screwed to the wall in a recess chopped out of the plaster and brickwork.

Alternatively, you can use an architrave-switch mounting box. This is a slim box that leaves plenty of room on each side for the wall-plug fixings needed for the light fitting.

Both mounting boxes are fixed to the wall like a flush-mounted socket.

The basic circuit and connections

The simplest way to connect wall lights to the lighting circuit is via a junction box. The procedure is to complete the wall-light installation first, then switch off the electricity and connect the new installation with the junction box.

Wire up a one-way switch. All the wall lights in the room will be controlled by this switch, though if you choose lights that have integral switches they can be controlled individually too.

Next, run a 1mm² two-core-and-earth cable from the junction box, looping in and out of each wall-light mounting to the last one, where the cable ends.

Prepare the cut ends of the conductors for connection. At each of the lights, slip green-and-yellow sleeving over the earth wires and connect them to the earth terminal on the mounting box (1).

Connect up the red and black wires to a block connector inside each light fitting: the black conductors to the terminal holding the blue wire, and the red ones to the terminal holding the brown wire (1).

The last wall-light mounting will have one end of the cable entering it. Strip and prepare the ends of the wires, then connect them as described above.

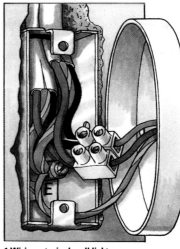

1 Wiring a typical wall light

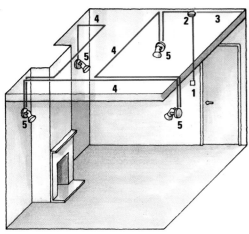

Basic wall-light circuit
The basic circuit and connections are as described above.
1 Switch
2 Junction box
3 Existing lighting circuit
4 Wall-light cable
5 Wall light

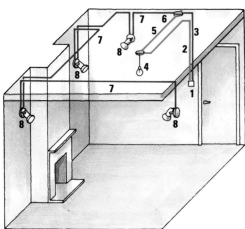

Ceiling light plus wall lights
If you want to retain your ceiling light, you can substitute a double-gang switch for the single one, and wire the present ceiling-light cable to one half of the switch and the new wall-lighting cable to the other half.
1 Double-gang switch
2 Old switch cable
3 New switch cable
4 Ceiling light
5 Existing lighting circuit
6 Junction box
7 1mm² wall-light cable
8 Wall light

Replacing a ceiling light
You can dispense with a ceiling light in favour of wall lights, using the existing wiring and switch. Switch off the power, then remove the rose and connect up the wiring to a fixed junction-box.
1 Existing switch and cable
2 Junction box replaces rose
3 Existing lighting circuit
4 1mm² wall-light cable
5 Wall light

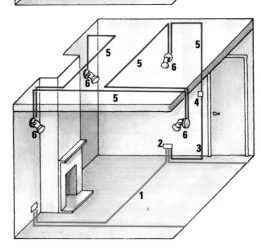

Using a spur
Wall lights can be wired to a ring circuit by means of a spur cable. Run a 2.5mm² two-core-and-earth spur from a nearby socket to a switched fused connection unit that has a 3amp fuse.
1 Ring circuit
2 Socket outlet
3 Spur cable
4 Fused connection unit
5 1mm² wall-light cable
6 Wall light

USING
ELECTRICITY
OUTDOORS

SEE ALSO

Details for:
Wiring Regulations	8
Switching off	16
RCD	17
Running cable	23-25
Running a spur	31
Lighting circuits	45
Junction box	46
One-way switch	50
Adding new light	51
Connecting to loop-in rose	51
Circuit lengths	58

● **Cutting through electrical flex**
If you accidentally cut the flex that services a power tool, switch off and unplug the tool before you inspect it or touch the severed flex.

Porch-light circuit
1 Loop-in circuit and switch cables
2 Ceiling rose
3 1mm² lighting cable
4 Junction box
5 Porch light
6 Switch cable
7 Porch-light switch

There are good reasons for extending your electrical installation outside the house. First, and most important, it is safer to run electric garden tools from a convenient, properly protected socket than to trail long leads from sockets inside the house – a practice that can lead to serious accidents.

A garage or workshop is also safer, and more efficient, if it is equipped with good lighting and its own circuit from which to run power tools.

Finally, well-arranged spot or floodlighting and waterfalls or fountains powered by electric pumps can add considerably to the charm of a garden or patio and extend its use in summer by providing a pleasing background for barbecues and outdoor parties.

SAFETY OUTDOORS

The need for absolute safety outdoors cannot be overemphasized. Damp conditions and the fact that users are likely to be in direct contact with the earth can result in fatal accidents if you don't follow the correct procedures.

● Install only light fittings specifically made for outside use.

● Use only cables recommended in the Wiring Regulations, and check their condition regularly.

● Protect all outside installations with residual current devices (RCDs), as they provide an almost instantaneous response to earth-leakage faults.

● Always disconnect the power before servicing electrical equipment and tools. Don't handle pool lighting or pumps unless the power has been switched off.

● Wear thick rubber-soled footwear when you use electric garden tools.

● Choose double-insulated power tools for extra protection.

Fitting a porch light

A light that illuminates the front or back entrance to your home suggests a welcoming atmosphere to visitors and helps them to identify the house. It also enables you to view unexpected callers before you open the door.

Fit only a light specifically designed for outdoor use. The fitting should be weatherproof, and the lamp or bulb itself should be held in a moisture-proof rubber gasket or cup that surrounds the electrical connections.

If possible, position the porch light in such a way that the cable to it can be run straight through the wall or ceiling of the porch directly into the back of the fitting. But if you do have to run ordinary cable along an outside wall, it should be protected by being passed through a length of plastic conduit.

Wiring procedure
A porch light is installed by a procedure very similar to that for adding a new light indoors. Take your power from the nearest ceiling rose – probably in the entrance hall – and run it to a 5amp four-terminal junction box screwed to a board between ceiling joists.

From the junction box, run a 1mm² two-core-and-earth cable to a switch mounted near the door, and a similar cable to the light fitting itself. Using a large masonry drill, bore a hole through the wall where you plan to position the light. Cement a short length of plastic conduit into the hole, using a soft rubber grommet to seal each end of the tube. Run the cable through the conduit; wire it into the fitting, following the manufacturer's instructions; and then, with the power switched off, connect the new porch-light cable at the ceiling rose.

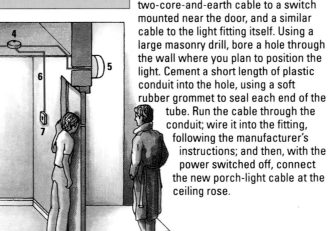

INSTALLING A SOCKET FOR GARDEN TOOLS

Many people plug garden tools into the nearest indoor socket – which often results in long extension leads trailing across the kitchen or living room out into the garden. A lead that is likely to cause someone to trip is dangerous – and, even more importantly, the Wiring Regulations stipulate that any socket outlet supplying mains power to garden tools or equipment must be protected by a residual current device (RCD) with a trip rating of 30 milliamps. This device automatically switches off the power as soon as it detects a fault, before anyone who is using the equipment can receive a fatal electric shock.

Sockets can be mounted outside the house provided that they are protected from the weather, although the special procedures involved are best left to a qualified electrician. But you can install a socket in a weatherproof workshop or garage, or lobby or conservatory that's part of the house by running a spur from a ring circuit. Mount it high enough to avoid being struck by a wheelbarrow or hidden by sacks or garden tools.

You can provide RCD protection in several ways. Perhaps the best method is to have a consumer unit with its own built-in residual current device or fit a separate RCD near the consumer unit so that it protects the whole ring circuit, including a spur for garden equipment. Alternatively, install a socket that incorporates an RCD (**1**). RCDs fitted in adaptors (**2**) or plugs provide some protection, but they do not satisfy the requirement in the Regulations for the socket itself to be protected.

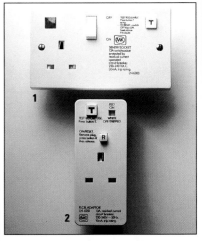

1 Socket with built-in RCD
2 Adaptor RCDs plug into any socket outlet

GARDEN LIGHTING AND PUMPS

SEE ALSO
Details for:
Corrugated
plastic sheet   61

Just a few outdoor light fittings can transform a garden dramatically. Spot or floodlights can emphasize particularly attractive features, at the same time providing functional lighting for pathways and steps, while strings of light bulbs woven through foliage afford attractive background illumination. The most impressive effects are produced with underwater lights, which can make small pools or fountains the focal points of a garden.

Extra-low-voltage lighting

A number of garden light fittings can be powered directly from mains electricity, though they need to be installed by a professional electrician. However, you can install light fittings or a complete lighting kit yourself if they connect up to an extra-low-voltage transformer.

Store the transformer under cover in a garage or workshop, close to a 13amp socket outlet, and connect it to the socket by an ordinary square-pin plug. The flex, which is normally supplied with the light fitting, is connected to the two 12 volt outlet terminals on the transformer. Carry out the connections to the lights following the instructions supplied by the manufacturer.

Unless the makers state otherwise, extra-low-voltage flex supplying garden lights can be run along the ground without further protection, but inspect it regularly and don't let it trail over stone steps or other sharp edges that could damage the PVC insulation if someone steps on it. If you have to add extra flex, use a waterproof connector.

Pool lighting

Pool lights are normally submerged so as to have at least 18mm (¾in) of water above their lenses. Some are designed to float unless they are held below the surface by smooth stones placed carefully on the flex.

Submerged lights get covered by the particles of debris that float in all ponds. To clean the lenses without removing the lights from the water, simply direct a gentle hose over them.

Occasionally you will have to remove a light and wash the lens thoroughly in warm soapy water. Always disconnect the power supply before you handle the lights or take them out of the pond.

Run the flex for pool lighting under the edging stones via a drain made from corrugated plastic sheeting. The entire length of the flex can be protected from adverse weather by being run through a length of ordinary garden hose. Take the safest route to the power supply, anchoring the flex gently in convenient spots – but do not cover it with soil or grass in case someone inadvertently cuts through it with a spade or fork. Join lengths of low-voltage cable with waterproof connectors.

Pumps

Electric pumps in garden pools provide fountains and waterfalls. A combination unit will send an adjustable jet of water up into the air, at the same time pumping water through a plastic tube to the top of a rockery to trickle back into the pool.

Some pumps run directly from the mains supply. To fit these, follow the manufacturer's instructions and consult an electrician. But there are also extra-low-voltage pumps that connect to a transformer shielded from the weather (see left). So you can disconnect the pump without disturbing the extra-low-voltage wiring to the transformer, join two lengths of cable with a waterproof connector. Conceal the connector under a stone or gravel beside the pool.

Most manufacturers recommend you take a pump from the water at the end of each season, clean it thoroughly, then return it to the water immediately. To avoid corrosion, don't leave it out of the water for very long without cleaning and drying it. Never service a pump without first disconnecting it from the power supply. During the winter, run the pump for an hour every week to keep it in good working condition.

● **Extra-low-voltage**
This is the strictly correct term to describe equipment that runs on 50V or less. However, manufacturers and suppliers often use the term low-voltage to describe similar equipment.

Waterproof cable connector
A suitable cable connector is available from pump and lighting suppliers.

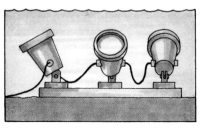
Stand underwater floodlights on a flat stone

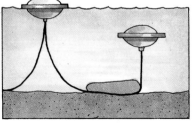
Place a stone on the cable to submerge a light

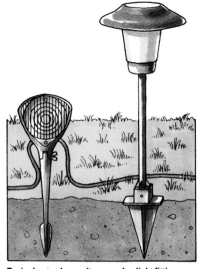
Typical extra-low-voltage garden light fittings

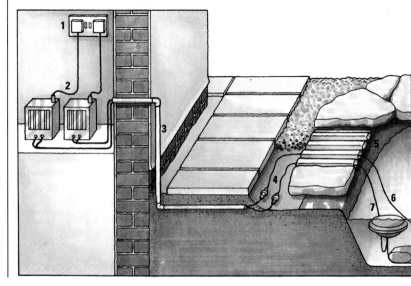

Pump and lighting circuits
1 Socket outlet
2 BS3535 Type 3 isolating transformers
3 Plastic conduit
4 Waterproof connectors
5 Home-made drain
6 Pump cable
7 Lighting cable

RUNNING
POWER TO
OUTBUILDINGS

SEE ALSO
Details for:
PVC-insulated cable   22

The power supply to a separate workshop, garage or toolshed cannot be tapped from other domestic circuits.

    The cable must run from a switchfuse unit or from its own fuseway in the consumer unit and pass safely underground or overhead to the outside location – where it has to be wired into a switchfuse unit from which the various circuits in the outbuilding can be distributed as required.

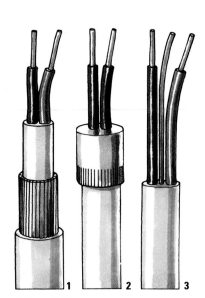

Outdoor cables
1 Armoured cable
2 Mineral-insulated copper-sheathed cable
3 PVC-insulated-and-sheathed cable

Types of cable permitted outdoors

Three types of cable can be used outside. The type you choose will depend on how you wish to run the cable.

Armoured cable
This two-core or three-core cable is insulated in the ordinary way but is also protected by a steel-wire armour, which is itself insulated with an outer sheath of PVC. In the two-core cable the wire armour provides the path to earth, but some authorities insist on three-core cable, which has an earth wire.

    Armoured cable is expensive, and must be terminated at a special junction box at each end of its run where it can be connected to ordinary PVC-insulated cable. It is fitted with threaded glands for attaching it to the junction boxes. This type of cable needs no additional protection when buried in the ground.

Mineral-insulated copper-sheathed cable
The only other cable that can be buried without additional protection is mineral-insulated copper-sheathed (MICS) cable. This has bare copper conductors

tightly packed in magnesium-oxide powder within a copper sheathing. The copper sheathing can act as the earth conductor, and is itself sheathed in PVC insulation. Because the mineral powder absorbs moisture, special seals must be fitted at the ends of the cable.

    Like armoured cable, MICS cable is expensive and must be terminated at special junction boxes in order to use cheaper cable in the outbuilding itself.

PVC-insulated-and-sheathed cable
Ordinary PVC-insulated two-core-and-earth cable can be run underground to an outbuilding providing it is protected against damage by being enclosed in an impact-resistant plastic conduit. If it has to go round corners, elbow joints are cemented onto the ends of straight runs of conduit. The electrical cable itself can be continuous. This is a much cheaper way of taking power to an outbuilding than installing armoured or MICS cable.

    PVC-insulated cable can also be run overhead quite safely under certain specified conditions (see below).

Ways of running outdoor cable

Underground
Running cable underground is usually the best way of supplying electricity to an outbuilding.

    You should bury the cable in a trench at least 500mm (1ft 8in) deep, or deeper still if the cable has to pass under vegetable plots or other areas where digging is likely to go on.

    It's best to plan your cable run so as to avoid such areas wherever possible. But you can provide extra protection for the cable by laying housebricks along both sides of it to support a covering made from pieces of paving slab. You can also bury special black-and-yellow-striped tape to serve as a warning to anyone who happens to uncover the slabs at a later date.

    Line the bottom of the trench with finely sifted soil or sand, lay the cable, and then carefully fill in.

Overhead
Ordinary PVC-insulated cable can be run from house to outbuilding provided that it is at least 3.5m (12ft) above the ground or 5.2m (17ft) above a driveway that's accessible to vehicles. The cable may not be used unsupported over a distance of more than 3m (10ft), though the same distance can be spanned by running the cable through a continuous length of rigid steel conduit suspended at a height of at least 3m (10ft) above the ground or 5.2m (17ft) above a drive-way. The conduit itself must be earthed.

    Over greater distances, the cable must be supported by a metal catenary wire stretched taut between the house and outbuilding. The supporting wire must be earthed. The cable is clipped to it or hung from slings.

    PVC-insulated cable can also be run through conduit mounted on a wall.

Protecting underground cable
Support paving slabs on bricks to protect a cable at the bottom of a trench.

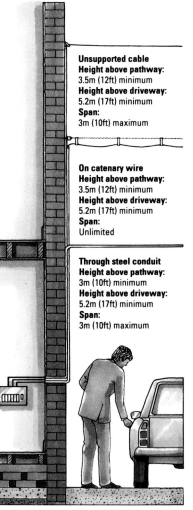

Unsupported cable
Height above pathway:
3.5m (12ft) minimum
Height above driveway:
5.2m (17ft) minimum
Span:
3m (10ft) maximum

On catenary wire
Height above pathway:
3.5m (12ft) minimum
Height above driveway:
5.2m (17ft) minimum
Span:
Unlimited

Through steel conduit
Height above pathway:
3m (10ft) minimum
Height above driveway:
5.2m (17ft) minimum
Span:
3m (10ft) maximum

Running cable overhead

A variety of equipment and cables can be used to run a circuit to an outbuilding. The method described here uses normal PVC-insulated cable and a switchfuse unit at each end of the circuit – but you can start in a spare fuseway in the consumer unit if one is available.

It is assumed that sockets and lighting are required in the outbuilding, so the lighting circuit is taken from the power cable via a junction box and an unswitched fused connection unit. Run the cable underground in impact-resistant plastic conduit, entering both buildings above the DPC and, if possible, beneath the floorboards.

House end of the circuit

Mount a 30amp switchfuse unit near the meter and then fit a 30amp circuit fuse. Install a residual current device between the unit and the meter.

Next, run 10mm^2 two-core-and-earth cable from the 'Load' terminals of the RCD to the 'Mains' terminals of the switchfuse unit. Connect the outgoing 4mm^2 cable to the 'Load' terminals (1) of the switchfuse unit.

Prepare one red and one black 16mm^2 PVC-sheathed-and-insulated cable for the meter leads and attach them to the 'Mains' terminals of the RCD.

Wire a 16mm^2 earth lead to the RCD (1) in readiness for connection to the consumer's earth terminal. Don't try to make the connections to the meter and Company's earth yourself – they must be made by the Electricity Company.

Outbuilding end of circuit

Run a 4mm^2 two-core-and-earth cable through conduit from the house to the outbuilding, terminating at a 30amp switchfuse unit mounted on the wall.

Connect up the incoming cable to the supply or 'Mains' terminals of the switchfuse unit and the outgoing 4mm^2 cable to its 'Load' terminals (2), then run

this cable to the outbuilding's sockets.

Insert a 30amp junction box at some point along the power cable (3), and run a 4mm^2 spur from it to an unswitched fused connection unit fitted with a 3amp fuse; then run 1mm^2 two-core-and-earth cable from the connection unit to the light fitting and switch.

SEE ALSO
Details for:
Running cable	23-25
Connecting sockets	30
Fused connection unit	34
Lighting circuits	45
Lighting junction box	46
One-way switch	50

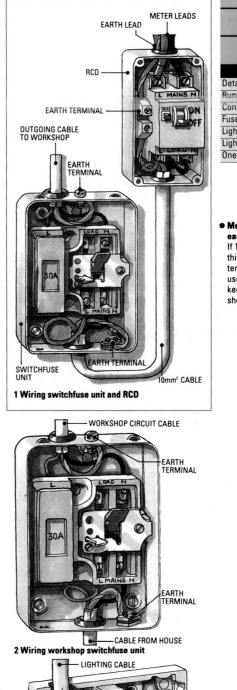

HOUSE END OF CIRCUIT

1 Wiring switchfuse unit and RCD

● **Meter leads and earth lead**
If 16mm^2 cable is too thick for the terminals in the RCD, use 10mm^2 cable but keep the leads as short as possible.

2 Wiring workshop switchfuse unit

3 Wiring junction box on power circuit

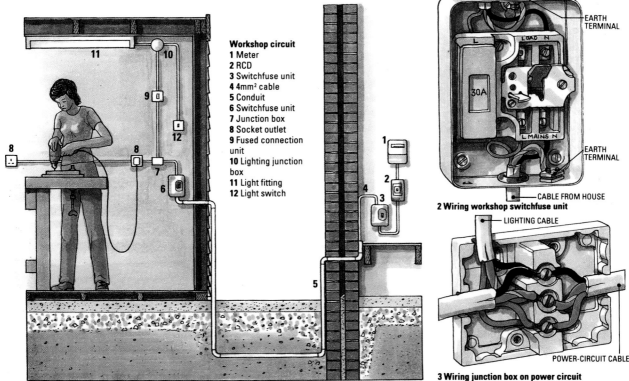

Workshop circuit
1 Meter
2 RCD
3 Switchfuse unit
4 4mm^2 cable
5 Conduit
6 Switchfuse unit
7 Junction box
8 Socket outlet
9 Fused connection unit
10 Lighting junction box
11 Light fitting
12 Light switch

COMPLETE WIRING

SEE ALSO

Details for:
RCD	17
Consumer unit and fuses	18–19
Lighting circuits	21
Power circuits	21
Fixed appliances	34–45

Planning ahead

As an amateur, before deciding to take on the complete rewiring of your house yourself, it is advisable to consider the time factor very carefully. When you are working on only one circuit, the rest of the household can function normally, but to renew all the circuits running to the house's consumer unit means that eventually every part of your home will be affected by the work.

A full-time professional can cope with all this in such a way that the level of inconvenience and disruption to the household is kept to a minimum. But the amateur, perhaps obliged to work only at weekends, will almost certainly have to think in terms of a time span lasting several weeks – especially since it is very important not to work hastily on such installations, as hurried work can lead to dangerous mistakes.

So unless you are very experienced and are able to make the installation a full-time commitment for a week or two, you would be well advised to employ a fully qualified electrician to undertake this time-consuming job.

He or she may perhaps be willing to work alongside you, enabling you to save considerably on the cost by doing some of the jobs that have nothing to do with electrical work – such as running cable under floors and channelling out plaster and brickwork.

Circuits: maximum lengths

The maximum length of a circuit is limited by the permitted voltage drop and the time it takes to operate the fuse or MCB in the event of an earth fault.

The method for calculation given in the Wiring Regulations is extremely complicated, but the table below will provide you with a simple method for determining the maximum cable lengths for common domestic circuits.

If necessary, split up your circuits so that none of the indicated cable lengths are exceeded. If your requirements fall outside the limits of this chart, then ask a professional electrician to make the calculations for you.

Rewirable fuses are not included as they are subject to special restrictions, which make them an unwise choice.

Most two-core-and-earth cables have a standard-size protective circuit conductor (earth wire). In each case, the chart shows the size of earth wire used in the calculations.

The maximum circuit lengths given in the chart are based on the assumption that you won't install any cables where the ambient temperature exceeds 30°C (86°F), that no more than two cables will be bunched together, and that you will not cover any of the cables with thermal insulation. The shower-circuit lengths assume that a 30 milliamp RCD is used in the circuit.

MAXIMUM LENGTHS FOR DOMESTIC CIRCUITS

TYPE OF CIRCUIT	Max. floor area	Cable size in mm²	Size of earth wire in mm²	USING FUSES		USING MCBs	
				Current rating of circuit fuse	Max. cable length using cartridge fuse	Current rating of MCB	Max. cable length using MCB
RING CIRCUIT	100sq m	2.5	1.5	30amp	60m	32amp	50m
RADIAL CIRCUIT	20sq m	2.5	1.5	20amp	35m	20amp	33m
	50sq m	4	1.5	30amp	38m	32amp	15m
COOKER with socket outlet		4	1.5	30amp	20m	32amp	15m
		6	2.5	30amp	38m	32amp	24m
IMMERSION HEATER up to 3kW		2.5	1.5	15amp	40m	16amp	38m
SHOWER up to 9.6kW		10	4	45amp	20m	40amp	20m
STORAGE HEATER		2.5	1.5	15amp	35m	16amp	30m
STORAGE FAN HEATER		4	1.5	30amp	24m	32amp	34m
FIXED LIGHTING excluding switch drops		1	1	5amp	95m	6amp	95m
		1.5	1	5amp	110m	6amp	110m

DESIGNING YOUR SYSTEM

Before discussing your requirements with a professional, you need to form clear ideas about the kind of installation you want. Although you may eventually decide between you to change some of the details, a proper specification can help the electrician considerably and will also enable you to avoid expensive additions and modifications.

Choosing the best consumer unit

It is worth installing the best consumer unit you can afford. Choose one that has cartridge fuses or miniature circuit breakers (MCBs), and make sure it has enough spare fuseways for possible additional circuits.

Residual current devices

Ask the electrician about the value of installing a residual current device (RCD). You could have one built into your consumer unit.

Power circuits

Ring circuits are better than radial circuits for supplying socket outlets. Provided that the floor area in question does not exceed 100sq m (120sq yds), you can have as many sockets as you like – so make sure your plan includes enough outlets to meet your present and likely future needs. Economizing on the cost of a few sockets now could cause you considerable inconvenience in the future, if you have to start adding spurs to the system.

Lighting circuits

Modern domestic lighting circuits are normally designed round a loop-in system; but remember that, if expedient, individual light fittings can be supplied from a junction box.

You should insist on a lighting circuit for each floor – so that you will never be left totally without electric lights if a fuse should blow.

In the interests of safety, make sure that you have two-way or three-way switches installed for lights in passageways and on landings and staircases.

Additional circuits

If you are having your whole house rewired, consider installing extra radial circuits for appliances such as immersion heaters and electrically heated showers.

SEE ALSO
Details for:
Heater circuits   40-41

One good reason for the popularity of electric storage heaters is their use of cheap night-time power. Indeed, the Electricity Companies' special rate for off-peak power can be as little as half that charged for daytime supply, or even less. This cut-rate scheme is called Economy 7, referring to the seven hours of the night when the cheap rate is in force.

The night-time power heats up a core of firebrick or similar material in the storage heater, and the core releases the heat next day – a process of convection whereby cool air is drawn in at the bottom of the heater, to be warmed as it passes over the hot core and expelled from the top.

The refined lines of modern storage heaters look at home in any interior

Types of storage heater

The early storage heaters were bulky and space-consuming; and they emitted heat at a set rate, so the user had no control over the output. The heat stored during the night could be adjusted – but this involved making an estimate of the next day's heating requirements, and a sudden change of weather could leave the user with too much or too little heat.

Recent advances in storage-heater technology and design have improved their appeal considerably. Modern ones are slimmer – some are just 150mm (6in) deep – and may either be wall-mounted or freestanding. They also have better insulation and allow greater control of heat output. Adjustable dampers and fans (some thermostatically controlled) enable the modern units to be run at low levels in unoccupied rooms and opened up when needed – even late in the day, when the older type of storage heater would run out of stored heat.

Some units retain a residue of stored heat, which reduces overnight charging and cuts costs further. Others monitor room temperatures at night, assess the next day's heating needs (a cold night is normally followed by a cold day) and adjust the heat charge accordingly.

Positioning storage heaters

Like radiators, storage heaters should be placed below single-glazed windows to counter draughts and balance the room temperature. With double glazing, they can go anywhere that's convenient and, if possible, should be positioned to give the best heat spread. The heaters have individual circuits and a separate consumer unit, plus an off-peak meter to record their power consumption.

HOW MANY STORAGE HEATERS?

To work out the ideal number of storage heaters for your home really accurately, together with the optimum output, you would have to calculate your needs in the same way as when planning a wet central-heating system with radiators. With this process the heating requirements of each room have to be worked out in detail, and then heaters selected to meet those demands.

Ready-reckoner charts

However, installing storage heaters is a much easier undertaking than putting in a full central-heating system – in fact, it is a very common DIY job. Guides for the amateur are therefore provided by the Electricity Companies and by some manufacturers. These take the form of simple charts that help you to estimate each room's requirements on the basis of the floor area and number of outside walls. Although charts of this kind are not completely accurate, they at least help you to choose heaters from the sizes that are most commonly available.

Selecting the optimum number

But there is an even simpler method for deciding the optimum number of storage heaters for your home.

If your total night-time load (including water heating) exceeds 14.4kW, then the 60amp service-cable fuse will be overloaded – and, if that happens, your Electricity Company may insist on a hefty contribution towards the cost of reinstating the service. However, within this limit you can safely install one small (1.7kW), one medium-size (2.5kW) and two large (3.4kW) storage heaters.

Place one of the large heaters in the hall and the other in your main living room. (In a small flat, these may be the only storage heaters that are needed). The medium-size heater can be placed in your second most important downstairs room, and the small heater should supply adequate warmth for your main bedroom. You can then use convection heaters or 'direct' oil-filled radiators to heat any other rooms and to provide top-up heating for the principal rooms of your house or flat.

With this type of system something like 90 per cent of your total heating will be supplied at the cheap off-peak rate, and consequently your overall running costs will be reasonable.

SEE ALSO
Details for:	
Double insulation	8
Using a tester	9
Supplementary bonding	10
Stripping flex	13
Stripping cable	22
Running cable	23-25
Drilling joists	25

Torch
Keep a torch handy for checking your consumer unit when a fuse blows on a lighting circuit. You may also need artificial light when working on connections below floorboards or in the loft, and a torch that stands unsupported is particularly helpful.

Electrician's skate

Diagonal cutters

● **Essential tools**
  Terminal
  screwdrivers
  Wire cutters
  Wire strippers
  Power drill and bits
  Torch
  General-purpose
  tools

ELECTRICIAN'S TOOL KIT
You need only a fairly limited range of tools to make electrical connections, but an extensive general-purpose tool kit is required for making cable runs and for fixing electrical accessories and appliances to the structure of the house.

SCREWDRIVERS

Buy good screwdrivers for tightening electrical terminals. Cheap ones are practically useless, being made from such soft metal that the tips soon twist out of shape.

Terminal screwdriver
A terminal screwdriver has a long, slim cylindrical shaft that is ground to a flat tip.

For turning screw terminals in sockets and larger appliances, buy a screwdriver with a plastic handle and a plastic insulating sleeve on its shaft.

Use a smaller screwdriver with a very slim shaft to work on ceiling roses or to tighten plastic terminal blocks in small fittings.

Cabinet screwdriver
You will need a woodworking screwdriver to fix mounting boxes to walls.

SKATE

A skate is made with a cutting disc that severs the joint between tongue-and-groove floorboards. Run the tool back and forth with one foot.

WIRE CUTTERS

Use wire cutters for cropping cable and flex to length.

Electrician's pliers
These are engineer's pliers with insulating sleeves shrunk onto their handles. Use them for cropping circuit conductors and for twisting their ends together.

Diagonal cutters
Diagonal cutters will crop thick conductors more effectively than electrician's pliers – although you may need a junior hacksaw to cut meter leads.

WIRE STRIPPERS

There are various tools for cutting or stripping the plastic insulation that covers cables and flexible cords.

Wire strippers

Wire strippers
To remove the insulation from cable and flex, use a pair of wire strippers with jaws shaped to cut through the covering without damaging the wire core. There is a multi-purpose version that can both strip the insulation and crop conductors to length.

Sharp knife
A knife with sharp disposable blades is best for slitting and peeling the sheathing encasing cable and flex.

DRILLS

When you run circuit wiring, you need a drill with several special-purpose bits for boring through wood and masonry.

Auger
Some electricians employ a long wood-boring auger to drill through the wall head plate and noggings when they're running a switch cable from an attic down to its mounting box.

Power drill
A cordless power drill is often ideal for boring cable holes through timbers and for making wall-plug fixings. As well as standard masonry bits for wall fixings, you will need a much longer version for boring through brick walls and clearing access channels behind skirting boards.

If you shorten the shaft of a wide-tipped spade bit, you can use it in a power drill between floor joists instead of hiring a special joist brace.

TESTERS

Even when you have turned off the power at the consumer unit, use a tester to check that the circuit is safe to work on.

Electronic mains tester
Be sure to buy an electronic two-prong tester that is intended for use with mains voltage – similar devices are sold in auto shops for 12volt car wiring only.

Always check that the tester is functioning properly before and after you use it by testing it on a circuit you know to be live.

Following the manufacturer's instructions, place one probe on the neutral terminal and the other one on the live terminal to be tested. If the bulb illuminates, the circuit is live; if it does not illuminate, try again between the earth terminal and each of the live and neutral terminals. If the bulb still doesn't light up (and you've checked the tester), you can assume the circuit is not live.

Continuity tester
A continuity tester will test whether a circuit is complete or an appliance is properly earthed. Alternatively, buy a multi-tester that combines the functions of continuity testing and mains-voltage testing (see above).

Using a continuity tester
Switch off the power at the consumer unit before making the following test. To find the two ends of a buried disconnected cable, twist the black and red conductors together at one end, and then apply the tester's probes to the same conductors at the other end (1). Depress the circuit-testing button on the tester. The bulb should light up and, with some testers, there may also be an audible signal. Untwist the conductors. Make the test again – and if the bulb does not illuminate, the two ends belong to the same cable.

To check whether a plug-in appliance is safely earthed, apply one probe to the earth pin of the plug – the longest of the three – and touch an unpainted part of the metal casing of the appliance with the other probe (2). Depress the test button – if the earth connection is good,

then the bulb will illuminate.

Don't try to use the appliance if the bulb illuminates when you apply the probe to either of the plug's other pins (3). (Make sure the plug fuse is working.) Have a suspect appliance overhauled by an electrician.

You cannot test a double-insulated appliance, as it has no earth connection in the plug.

1 Apply a probe to each conductor

2 Test earth pin and casing

3 Test one other pin and casing

GENERAL-PURPOSE TOOLS

Every electrician needs tools for lifting and cutting floorboards, for fixing mounting boxes, and for cutting cable runs.

Claw hammer
For nailing cable clips to walls and timbers.
Club hammer
For use with a cold chisel.
Cold chisel
For cutting channels in plaster and brickwork in order to bury cables or mounting boxes.
Bolster chisel
For levering up floorboards.
Padsaw or power jigsaw
For cutting through floorboards close to skirtings.
Floorboard saw
This is the best tool for cutting across a prised-up board, though a tenon saw can be used instead.
Spirit level
For checking that mounting boxes are fixed horizontally.
Plasterer's trowel or filling knife
Either tool can be used for covering concealed cable with plaster or other kinds of filler.
Spanner
A small spanner is needed for making the earth connection in some appliances, and also for supplementary earth bonding.

Accessory
An electrical component permanently connected to a circuit – a switch, socket outlet, connection unit etc.

Adaptor
A device used to connect more than one appliance to a socket outlet.

Ampere (Amp)
A unit of measurement of the flow of electric current necessary to produce the required wattage for an appliance.

Appliance
A machine or device powered by electricity.

Catenary wire
A length of wire cable suspended horizontally between two points.

Ceiling rose
A special junction box for connecting a suspended light fitting to a lighting circuit.

Ceiling switch
A light switch attached to a ceiling and operated by a pull-cord.

Chase
A groove cut in masonry or plaster to accept an electrical cable. or To cut such grooves.

Circuit
A complete path through which an electric current can flow.

Circuit breaker
A special switch installed in a consumer unit to protect an individual circuit. Should a fault occur, the circuit breaker will switch off automatically.

Conductor
A component, usually a length of wire, along which an electric current will flow.

Consumer unit
A box, situated near the meter, which contains the fuses or MCBs protecting all the circuits. It also houses the main isolating switch that cuts the power to the whole building.

Corrugated plastic sheet
A lightweight PVC sheet used to roof outbuildings and lean-to extensions.

Dimmer switch
A switch that changes the level of illumination by varying the electric current through a lamp.

Double-pole switch
A switch that breaks both the live and neutral conductors.

Downlighter
A type of ceiling-mounted light fitting that directs a relatively narrow beam of light to the floor.

Draw wire
A flexible wire or steel tape used to pull electric cable through confined spaces.

Earth
A connection between an electrical circuit and the earth (ground). A terminal to which a connection is made.

Earth-leakage circuit breaker – ELCB
See RCD

Extension
A length of electrical flex for temporarily connecting the short permanent flex of an appliance to a wall socket.

Fuse
A protective device containing a thin wire that is designed to melt at a given temperature caused by an excess flow of current on a circuit.

Fuseboard
Where the main electrical service cable is connected to the house circuitry. The accumulation of consumer unit, meter etc.

Grommet
A ring of plastic or rubber lining a hole to protect an electrical cable from chafing.

Immersion heater
An electrical element designed to heat water in a storage cylinder.

Insulation – electrical
Nonconductive material surrounding electrical wires or connections to prevent the passage of electricity.

Insulation – thermal
Materials used to reduce the transmission of heat.

Miniature circuit breaker – MCB
See Circuit breaker.

Neutral
The section of an electrical circuit which carries the flow of current back to source. A terminal to which connection is made.

Nogging
A short horizontal wooden member between studs in a timber-framed wall.

Phase
The part of an electrical circuit which carries the flow of current to an appliance or accessory. More commonly known as live.

Protective multiple earth – PME
A system of electrical wiring in which the neutral part of the circuit is used to take earth-leakage current to earth.

Radial circuit
A power circuit feeding a number of socket outlets or fused connection units and terminating at the last accessory.

Residual-current circuit breaker – RCCB
See RCD

Residual current device – RCD
A device which monitors the flow of electric current through the live and neutral wires of a circuit. When it detects an imbalance caused by earth leakage, it cuts off the supply of electricity as a safety precaution.

Ring circuit
A continuous power circuit starting at and returning to the consumer unit. Also known as ring main.

Rising main
The pipe which supplies water under mains pressure, usually to a storage cistern in the roof.

Rocker switch
A modern-style switch operated by a lever which pivots about its centre.

Sheathing
The outer layer of insulation surrounding an electrical cable or flex.

Short circuit
The accidental rerouting of electricity to earth which increases the flow of current and blows a fuse.

Spotlight
A light fitting which directs a narrow beam of illumination onto a specific object or area of wall or floor.

Spur
A short length of cable that feeds a socket outlet or fused connection unit by taking its power via another similar accessory.

Storage heater
A space-heating device that stores heat generated by cheap night-rate electricity, then releases it during the following day.

Studs
The vertical members of a timber-framed wall.

Supplementary bonding
The connecting to earth of exposed metal appliances and pipework in a bathroom or kitchen.

Terminal
A connection for an electrical conductor.

Toggle switch
An old-fashioned light switch that is operated by a short projecting lever.

Transformer
A device which increases or decreases voltage on an electrical circuit.

Uplighter
A light fitting that reflects illumination onto a ceiling.

Volt
A unit of measurement of 'pressure' provided by Electricity Company generators and which drives the current along the conductors.

Wiring Regulations
A code of professional practice laid down by the Institution of Electrical Engineers.

Page numbers in *italics* refer to photographs and illustrations

A

accessory 61
adaptors 27, 61
 RCCB 54; *54*
ampere (amp) 9, 61
appliance 61
appliances
 cookers 37
 door bells 42
 earthing 10
 fixed 34
 heaters 35
 immersion heaters 39
 showers 45
 small 36
 storage heaters 40-41
 telephone extensions 44
 TV aerials 43
architrave switch 49
armoured cable 56; *56*
artificial ventilation 11; *11*
auger 60; *60*

B

basic principles 8
bathroom
 heater 35
 lighting 51
 safety in 10
batten holder 47; *47*
bell 42
bell circuit 42; *42*
bell push 42
bell transformer 42
BESA box 48, 53; *48*
bonding to earth 10, 17; *16*
buckle clip 23; *23*
buzzer 42

C

cable connector 55; *55*
cables
 exterior-duty 56; *56*
 fixing 23; *23*
 old types 22
 running 23-5, 56; *23, 25, 56*
 sizes 22
 stripping 22
 types 22; *22*
 underfloor 24, 25; *24, 25*
 underground 56; *56*
cartridge fuse 19
 checking 20; *20*
cartridge-fuse carrier 19

catenary wire 56, 61; *56*
cavity-wall mounting box 34; *34*
ceiling rose 61
 connecting 46; *46*
 replacing 48
ceiling switch 61
 wiring 45, 51; *45, 51*
channel, cable 23; *23*
chase 61
chimes 42; *42*
circuit breaker 9, 19; *19*
circuits 8, 21, 61; *8, 21*
 maximum lengths 58
 see also lighting circuits; power circuits
clips, cable 23
close-mounted ceiling lights 47-8; *47, 48*
coaxial plugs, connecting 43; *43*
coiled flex 12; *12*
colour coding 8; *8*
combined lighting circuit 45; *45*
concealed fixing 23
conductors 8, 61
 connecting to plugs 13, *13*
conduit box 48; *48*
connection units, fused 34; *34*
consumer unit 16, 18, 58, 61; *16, 18*
 wiring 33, 41; *33, 41*
consumption records 6
continuity 33
continuity tester 60; *60*
controls 6
cooker
 control unit 37; *37*
 switchfuse unit 38; *38*
 terminal outlet box 37, 38; *37, 38*
 wiring 37-8; *37, 38*
cooker hood 36
copper, for wiring 8
corrugated plastic sheet 61
costs of electricity 6, 7
cross-bonding 17; *16, 17*
cutters 60; *60*

D

diagonal cutters 60; *60*
dial meters 6; *6*
digital meters 6
dimmer switch 49, 50, 61; *49, 50*
dishwasher, wiring 36
doorbells 42; *42*
double insulation 8; *8*
double-pole switch 39, 61; *39*
downlighter 48, 61; *48*

draw wire 61
drills 60

E

earth clamp 10, 17; *10, 17*
earth-leakage circuit breaker – ELCB
 see residual current device
earth tag 10, 17; *10, 17*
earth wire 8, 10
earthing 8, 10, 17, 61; *10*
economy measures 6
Economy 7 scheme 6, 59
 water heating 39
electric shock 11
Electricity Company
 installation testing 9, 26, 38
 connections 16, 38, 41, 57
 storage-heater meter 40
 see also Economy 7 scheme
Electrical Engineers, Institution of 8
electrical safety
 outdoor installations 54
 precautions 9, 10, 14, 16
electronic mains tester 9, 60; *9, 60*
element, for immersion heater 38, 39; *38, 39*
extension leads 14, 61; *14*
extractor fan 36; *36*

F

fan-assisted heater 41
fault checking 20
fixed appliances, wiring 34
flex
 choice 13
 coiled 12; *12*
 connectors 14; *14*
 extenders 14; *14*
 fabric-covered 46
 stripping and connecting 13
 types 12; *12*
flex connectors 14; *14*
flexible cord *see* flex
floorboards, lifting 24; *24*
fluorescent lights 47; *47*
 fitting 49; *49*
fridge *see* refrigerator
fuse board (fuse box) 16, 17, 61; *16, 17*
fuse carriers 18, 19; *18, 19*
fused connection unit 34; *34*
fuses 9, 15, 19, 61; *19*
 changing 20, 34; *20, 34*
 for plugs 15; *15*
 ratings 19
 types 19; *19*

G

garden supply
  see outbuilding supply
garden lighting 55; *55*
garden, socket for 54; *54*
grommet 25, 61

H

heat/light unit 35; *35*
heated towel rail 35; *35*
**heater, instantaneous
  water** 36
heater, wiring 35; *35*

I

IEE Regulations 8, 9, 10
immersion heater 61
  flex 13
  types 38; *38*
  wiring 39; *39*
installation assessment 26-7
installations, outdoor 54-7
**Institution of Electrical
  Engineers** 8, 9
insulation
  electrical 61
  thermal 61
isolating switch 16

J

junction box 31, 32; *31, 32*
junction-box system 21, 45,
  46; *21, 45*

L

lampholder, pendant 15; *15*
light fittings 47; *47*
light switches
  adding new 51; *51*
  replacing 50
  types 49; *49*
  wiring 50
lighting circuits 21, 45, 58;
  21, 45
  checking *46*
  identifying conductors
  46; *46*
lights, adding 51-3; *51, 52, 53*
loop-in system 21, 45, 46;
  21, 45
low-voltage lighting 55

M

main switch equipment
  16; *16*
MCB *see* miniature circuit
  breaker
meter leads 16, 22; *22*
meter reading 6
meters 6; *6, 16*
**mineral-insulated copper-
  sheathed (MICS) cable**
  56; *56*
miniature circuit breaker
  19, 20, 61; *19, 20*
  ratings 19, 38
  selecting 19
multi-purpose tool 13, 60

N

**National Inspection Council
  for Electrical Installation
  Contracting – NICEIC** 9
neutral 8, 61
nogging 61

O

off-peak rates 6
one-way switch 50; *50*
outbuilding supply 56-7;
  56, 57
outdoor cable running 56, 57;
  56, 57
overhead cable
  requirements 56

P

pendant lights 15, 47; *15, 47*
phase (electrical) 8, 61
pipes, need for earthing 8, 10
pliers, electrician's 60; *60*
plug
  types 15
  wiring 15; *15*
plumbing a shower 45
PME *see* protective multiple
  earth
pool lighting 55; *55*
porch light 54; *54*
power circuits 21, 58
power drill 60
professional electricians
  9, 58
**protective multiple earth –
  PME** 17, 61
pumps, pool 55; *55*
**PVC-insulated-and-sheathed
  cable** 22, 56; *22, 56*

R

radial circuits 21, 61; *21*
  conversion to ring circuits
  33; *33*
RCCB *see* residual-current
  device
recessed light 47; *47*
recovery position (first aid)
  11; *11*
refrigerator, wiring 36
**Regulations for Electrical
  Installations (IEE Wiring
  Regulations)** 8, 9, 10
**residual current device –
  RCD** 17, 18, 45, 54, 58, 61;
  17, 54
  adaptor-type RCD 54; *54*
RCD *see* residual current
  device
rewirable fuse 19; *19*
  checking 20; *20*
  rewiring 20; *20*
rewiring 58
ring circuits 21, 61; *21*
  adding a spur 31; *31*
  extending 32; *32*
ring main *see* ring circuit
rising main 61
rocker switch 49, 61; *49*
round-pin fitting 15; *15*
running costs, appliance 7

S

safety precautions 9, 14, 16
  bathroom 10
  outdoor installation 54
scorching *27*
screwdrivers 60; *60*
service cable *16*
service head 16
shaver socket 10, 36; *36*
sheathing 12, 61
shower, plumbing 45
shower unit, wiring 10,
  45; *45*
skate 24, 60; *60*
skew nailing 47
sleeving
  colour coded 22; *22*
  heat-resistant 48
small appliances, wiring
  36; *36*
socket outlets
  checking 27
  connecting 30; *30*
  flush-mounted 29; *29*
  replacing 30
  shaver 10, 36; *36*
  surface-mounted 28; *28*
  types 28; *28*

splitter 43
spotlight 47, 61
spurs 21, 61; *21*
   adding 31; *31*
   for wall lights 53; *53*
square-pin plugs *see*
   T for 13amp plugs
stairway lighting 52
storage heaters 40-41, 59,
   61; *40, 59*
   fan-assisted 40, 41
   optimum number 59
stripping
   cable 22; *22*
   flex 13; *13*
studs 61
supplementary bonding 10,
   61; *10*
surface fixing 23
switched connection unit
   34; *34*
switches 8
   adding 51; *51*
   in-line 14; *14*
   light *see* light switches
   replacing 50; *50*
   wiring 50; *50*
switchfuse unit 38, 57; *38, 57*
switching off the power 16
system design 58

T

13amp plugs 15; *15*
13amp sockets 28-9; *28, 29*
telephone extensions 44; *44*
terminals 13, 61; *13*
terminal outlet box 38; *38*
testers 9, 60; *9*
thermostats 6
   immersion heater 6, 38, 39;
   38, 39
three-way lighting 52; *52*
time switch 6
toggle switch 61
tool kit 60
tool-shed supply *see*
   outbuilding supply
torch 60; *60*
towel rail, heated 35; *35*
track lights 47; *47*
   fitting 48; *48*
trailing socket 14; *14*
transformer 61
   bell 42
   outdoors 55; *55*
TV aerials 43; *43*
two-gang switch 50; *50*
two-way lighting 52; *52*
two-way switch 50; *50*

U

underground cable
   requirements 56
uplighter 61

V

volt 9, 61

W

wall fixings 61
wall heater, wiring 35; *35*
wall lights 47; *47*
   adding 53; *53*
washing machine, wiring 36
waste-disposal unit 36
water heaters
   immersion 61
   instantaneous 36
water heating, night rate 39
waterproof cable connector
   55; *55*
watt 9
wire cutters 60; *60*
wire strippers 60; *60*
Wiring Regulations 8, 9,
   10, 61
workshop circuit 57; *57*
workshop lighting 57